Financial control

ENGINEERING MANAGEMENT

Series editor S. H. Wearne, BSc(Eng), PhD, FICE, Consultant, Director of Institution courses and in-company training

Editorial panel D. E. Neale, CEng, FICE; D. P. Maguire, BSc, FICE; D. J. Ricketts, BSc; J. V. Tagg, CEng, FICE; G. D. Cottam, BSc, CEng, FICE; J. C. Bircumshaw, CEng, MICE

ENGINEERING MANAGEMENT

Financial control

Edited by
Martin Barnes
Coopers & Lybrand Deloitte

Thomas Telford, London

Published by Thomas Telford Ltd, Thomas Telford House,
1 Heron Quay, London E14 9XF

First published 1990

British Library Cataloguing in Publication Data
Financial control
   1. Engineering industries. Financial management
   I. Barnes, Martin   II. Series
   620.00681

ISBN: 0 7277 1522 4

Typeset in Great Britain by MHL Typesetting Limited, Coventry
Printed and bound in Great Britain by Mackays of Chatham

Preface

The aim of this guide is to introduce civil engineers to financial control and how business and projects are financed. Generally, civil engineers first encounter financial control in connection with projects in which they are involved, such as the construction of a power station or a bridge. As their careers progress, they become more involved in financial control of the businesses which carry out such projects, and in time they may become responsible for management of a sector of the business in which they are engaged. These aspects of financial control will be dealt with in two parts: part 1 deals with control of a business, and part 2 with control of a project.

Chapter 1 begins a review of financial control of the business with an introduction to corporate planning and budgeting. Elements of accounting and hence control are introduced in chapter 2 where financial accounting is distinguished from management accounting. Some fundamental accounting concepts and methods are explained and a procedure for analysing company accounts is introduced. Part 1 concludes in chapter 3 with an explanation of the nature and purpose of an audit, followed by a review of external and internal auditing and a description of a contract audit.

Part 2 begins the treatment of the financial control of projects with an introduction to the financing of construction projects, covering types, methods and sources of finance and referring to recent developments which are important in financing public sector projects. Chapter 5 focuses on the considerations which are involved in project appraisal, and chapter 6 on the control of project costs. The guide concludes with a chapter on the control of claims and dealing with disputes which may arise in the course of a project.

Financial control is one of the principal functions of managers of projects. The others are control of the quality and performance of the finished project, and control of timing. In the discussion of financial control of projects, the functions of the project manager are frequently referred to. This approach demonstrates that effective financial control requires effective management of the project. This, in turn, requires the project management functions to be identified clearly and assigned. References to the project manager apply to the individual or team which is carrying out this function on behalf of the project employer or client. The project management function may be performed by members of the employer's staff, it may be delegated to a consulting engineer or it may be carried out by a professional project management firm. The term project manager is used to apply to each of these arrangements.

Acknowledgements

I am particularly grateful to the contributors to this guide and to Stephen Wearne who made a number of helpful comments on the manuscript. My contributers and I also wish to acknowledge the help we have received from David Bell, John Clarkson, Janet Eilbeck, Mark Hatcher and Brian Hornsby. Finally, we would like to record our indebtedness to Harriette McGinlay and her colleagues who cheerfully retyped what must have seemed to them an endless series of drafts.

Martin Barnes
26 October 1989

Contents

1 Corporate planning and budgeting

This chapter examines two aspects of organizational planning: the corporate plan, which usually covers a period of three to five years; and the annual budget, which looks at one year of that plan in much greater detail.

Corporate planning

Why corporate planning?

What is corporate planning, why is it important for businesses, large or small, and how does it help to improve performance? A corporate or business plan is a scheme for moving from a present position to where an organization wishes to be to meet its objectives. The approach for bridging this gap is frequently called a strategy. A plan must also show how a business will react to changing circumstances to ensure that its objectives are met. A plan may also be used as a basis for monitoring progress towards the objectives.

A forward-looking plan is necessary for all types and sizes of business, although the nature and level of detail involved will vary from one organization to another. The more important part of a plan is not the detailed figures but the quality of the thinking from which the figures are developed. It is important that planning is carried out by the managers involved in the activities of a business so that they can relate to the plan and feel that the plan is their plan.

Why a written plan?

If quality of thought is important, why produce a written, quantified plan, especially when writing it up will use scarce management resources and will not be easy? The main reasons are that putting a plan on paper helps an organization to decide what it wants to achieve, to communicate its ideas to others and to monitor future performance. A written plan should be brief, precise and quantitative. It can be very helpful for external discussions, for example with bankers and with potential clients or joint venture partners.

Planning

A method of business planning is shown in Fig. 1.1. It demonstrates that planning has to be an iterative process. The different stages of the process will now be explained.

Review of the current situation and external environment

This review is a detailed, forward-looking exercise undertaken to understand an organization. One technique is to look at its *strengths* and *weaknesses* and the *opportunities* and *threats* it faces from the external environment. This is also known as a SWOT analysis.

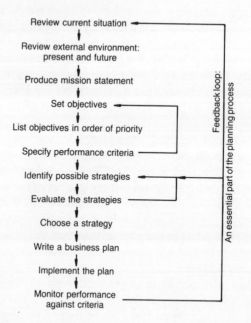

Fig. 1.1. Planning process

A review of strengths and weaknesses should cover the organization's products or services, resources, people, funds, new ideas, current and future skills and examine the organizational structure and ability of the organization to cope with change.

A useful technique for looking at products or services is a market segment analysis because it focuses attention on markets and their potential. A number of different factors should be considered for each market segment. In relation to the products or services both of the organization and its major competitors, the analysis should cover market share, profitability, reliance on segment, geographic spread, size, skills, market emphasis, style and future intentions. In relation to the major customers of the organization, the analysis should cover turnover and profit generated, buying characteristics and future intentions.

Customer perception

It is helpful to analyse how customers perceive the business in each market segment, taking into account matters such as business size, quality of service or product, completion of work on time and within budget, claims record, profitability and level of repeat business, so that buying characteristics and future intentions may be determined. It is also useful to consider how major potential customers perceive the major competitors of the business so that shortcomings can be identified and overcome.

The opportunities and threats posed by the external environment should also be considered. How are they expected to change over time, for example, in relation to new developments, market conditions, competitors, new legislation, exchange rates and political risks?

A SWOT analysis which has been carried out correctly provides a creative, forward-looking review which provides a balanced basis for considering possible future strategies.

Produce a mission statement and set objectives

A mission statement is a simple expression of the aims of a business in such terms as: 'to operate as a profitable, medium-sized civil engineering contractor in Gammashire.' Objectives must be set if the mission is to be capable of being achieved. Dissemination of these objectives should provide the business with a coherent policy to which management effort can be directed

3

properly. They should be expressed in a way which provides a means for assessing performance.

The number of objectives should be small and they should be acceptable to managers of the business, realistic in terms of resources and timing, firm, measurable and ranked so that any conflicts in implementation may be resolved. The objectives should identify elements of performance which will be monitored. These differ from one organization to another. The objectives must be based on medium- and long-term criteria as well as short-term criteria. Exploiting short-term profit without regard to effects on medium- and long-term performance, for example, could be very damaging in terms of lost demand.

Identification and evaluation of possible strategies

When the current and intended future positions have been established, the next step is to formulate alternative strategies to enable the business to move from one position to another. Initially all possible strategies should be identified, whether they are acceptable or not. Consideration of their acceptability comes later. Each strategy should be reviewed formally (with quantification) against the predetermined criteria.

There are several generically different strategies which can be used as a basis for determining the future direction of a business. For example, a strategy which focuses on low costs/margins requires large-scale operations, heavy investment, vigorous cost control and aggressive pricing to build market share. Possible benefits from this strategy are large profits from high turnover and economies of scale. On the other hand, a strategy which requires unique products or services based on advanced technology or features, may involve reduced turnover, reduced market share and perception of exclusivity (in relation to research and development, high quality customer support and good marketing). The possible benefits from this strategy are customer loyalty, exclusion of competitors, less price competition and increased profit margins.

Frequently neither of these strategies will be practical for smaller businesses. They often adopt a more targeted or specialized strategy as follows.

- *Focused*: develop a large market share in a narrow market segment; gain customer loyalty.

- *Differentiation*: develop a defensible niche in a market segment that is too small to interest large businesses.

- *Technical innovation*: expensive and high risk.

- *'Me too strategy'*: duplicate popular services or products of a large business but avoid promotion and development costs; position as a cheaper alternative.

- *Flexibility*: quick responses to changing market conditions and customer demand.

- *Others*: for example, lowest cost producer, market leader.

These generic strategies are illustrative. A series of appropriate and realistic strategies should develop for each organization.

After various strategies have evolved they should be evaluated against criteria such as

- internal consistency/organizational constraints
- o does the strategy match the values and attitudes of the principal implementors?

- consistency with the business environment
- o does the strategy match the current and future business environment?

- appropriateness to the resources of the organization
- o will limited resources be used most effectively?
- o does the strategy demand unobtainable resources?

- degree of risk
- o are the potential profits appropriate to the risks involved?

- timing
- o is the timing of the strategy correct?

- competitive reaction
- o will the strategy provoke a rapid and overwhelming reaction from competitors?
- o does the strategy allow for this reaction?

- workability
- o will the strategy achieve the objectives?
- o will the organization be able to implement the strategy, establish an appropriate organizational structure and systems

5

and apply the right leadership to gain commitment and motivation?

- sensitivity analysis
o how sensitive is the strategy to changes in assumptions about future conditions?

A preferred strategy should now emerge. It is then written up as the business strategy or plan together with a detailed plan for implementation. Responsibilities and a timetable must be specified. The timetable for implementation and ranking of criteria against which performance will be measured should be agreed as the strategy is written up. A successful strategy will protect the business as far as is possible from the competitive forces which are found in any business sector, such as supplier power, buyer power, threat of new entrants, threat of substitution and competitive rivalry.

With the benefit of hindsight it is possible at a later stage to determine whether the strategy provided a safeguard against these forces and, if not, whether the reasons were foreseen or at least foreseeable. Business plans rarely, if ever, match events as they unfold, but the planning process may be refined and improved by carrying out a review when the results are known.

Business planning is not easy but it is undoubtedly worthwhile. It will provide a framework for structured, creative thinking and produce a greater understanding of the business and of the markets and other conditions in which the business operates. Planning also helps to produce a mechanism for coping with change and focuses attention and effort on key issues. It can help to determine priorities to assist operational decision-making. It can anticipate problems and provide a means for reaching solutions. Business planning also provides a rational basis for measuring performance and helps managers to work as a team. In short, it will improve business performance.

Budgeting

A budget is a short- or long-term financial expression of an agreed plan. It should explicitly amplify policies which have been agreed as part of the business plan. Budgeting should not be a mechanical financial exercise. As a positive planning and decision-making tool, it should show, quantitatively, how agreed objectives will be achieved as well as their order of priority. The budget which has been set should be monitored regularly by comparing actual against planned income and expenditure and used as a basis for taking corrective action if needed.

Budget setting will now be described with reference to revenue budgeting (covering revenue expenditure). Capital budgeting (covering capital expenditure) will be dealt with at the end of this chapter.

Budget setting

The process of budget setting should be based on the requirements of the particular organization. The financial costs of various resources (such as costs of physical resources and labour) should be quantified and a statement of required expenditure over the period obtained. This expenditure is then adjusted by an iterative process of questioning and putting resources in order of priority until expenditure is reconciled with the available financial resources.

A construction company would start a budgeting process from the strategy laid down in the business plan, giving the size and number of jobs it expects to obtain in the given budget period. The company would also estimate the level and payment dates of revenue generated by the projects in which it is or may become involved. To be of maximum benefit, these estimates need to be as realistic as possible. When workload and revenue have been predicted as accurately as needed to meet objectives, all costs associated with projects must be defined. In this way it is possible to derive expected profits from the projects. This figure is then examined to see if it is satisfactory in terms of the management effort required, capital employed and risks involved, among other matters. If it is not, modification, if appropriate, to achieve a more realistic budget must take place.

If carried out correctly, budget setting provides an effective way of quantifying the performance required of existing or new operations. However, budget setting by itself is not sufficient. To complete the process actual performance must be compared against budgeted performance, any variations understood and action taken to bring the two into line. Taking positive corrective action converts monitoring into control.

In many organizations budgets are set by adjusting the budget for the previous year, adding a bit for inflation, and so on. This is mistaken because it allows errors to be repeated. It does not encourage control other than through the total cost and it limits the opportunities for a rational approach to budgeting. Budgets should be built up from their fundamental components; for example, four staff at £20 000 per annum gives staff costs of £80 000. This is often called zero based budgeting. Budget setting should be delegated to the manager who controls each function or service within an overall framework set by senior management. A timetable for budget setting is illustrated in Table 1.1. The objective is to start the budgeting process as late as possible in the preceding year while allowing budget-holders time to agree their budget before the start of the budget year.

Table 1.1   Budgeting timetable (based on March year end)

Step	Time/frequency
Budget setting	
Issue of budget guidelines to sector managers.	September
Sector managers distribute budget guidelines with their own additions to their budget-holders.	Late September
Budget-holders produce budgets.	October
Sector managers appraise budgets.	Early November
Sector managers produce consolidated budgets and narrative.	End November
Senior managers review sector budgets and consolidate.	Early December
During budget year Budget monitoring and control*	
Sector performance meeting with budget-holders.	Monthly
Sector managers report to senior manager.	Monthly
Senior manager performance meeting with sector managers.	Bi-monthly
Forecasts: estimating year-end position.	Quarterly

* Meeting and reporting dates should be set in advance of these events.

The framework set for the business as a whole should usually consist of two sections

- *Part 1*: general guidelines that apply to all sectors
- *Part 2*: specific guidelines for each function or service within each sector.

As an illustration, consider the case of a consulting engineering practice with four self-contained teams which specialize in different types of projects. Part 1 of the guidelines, which will have been agreed by senior management, will cover

- service aims, derived from the business plan
- any cross-team initiatives and how they will be treated (such as product, process or technique developments which overlap teams)
- an update on the firm's financial strategy if it has changed
- specific assumptions about
- o general salary increases
- o allocated cost increases

- availability of funds for investment
- a statement of the role of budgeting and how budgets are to be assembled
- required format.

Part 2 of the guidelines for each team should cover

- growth targets and new types of work as set out in the plan
- profitability targets
- cost improvement programmes.

The budget-holder (i.e. the person who is responsible for cost control against budgeted work content) then produces a budget in the agreed format. It is vital that assumptions about volume of work are clearly stated so that the effects of changed levels of volume may be understood.

Capital budgeting

As finance is a limited resource in any organization, its application should be carefully controlled. One of the most important methods of control is capital budgeting, which is a list of planned investment projects (capital expenditure) normally prepared by the company, division or other profit centre. A profit centre is any part of an organization to which both costs and income are attributed. Plans prepared using agreed criteria are then approved by the relevant senior managers.

The process of bringing a major investment project to fruition begins with the original concept or requirement which may be triggered by a company's business plan, new legislation or perceived external opportunities and threats. This is followed by an initial request for project authorization which will need to describe the project briefly, indicate approximate costs and likely benefits and contain an estimate of the cost of a feasibility study and its timing. An appraisal of the project follows whereby cost estimates, required capital expenditure, revenue generation and tax effects of each option are rigorously appraised and considered in the context of the overall objectives of the business. Final selection of the project, approval of the project for inclusion in the capital budget, setting of project implementation controls and post-audit review account for the remaining stages of the project cycle are covered in detail in chapter 5.

2 Accounting

Accounting is a means of communicating the financial impact of an organization's activities. An understanding of the subject will help the reader to communicate with people in the business community as well as with accountants and enable him or her to participate more effectively in financial decision-making. This chapter gives a broad overview of accounting practices in the UK. It defines accounting systems, distinguishes between financial and management accounting, provides an introduction to some fundamental accounting concepts and introduces the reader to a procedure for analysing company accounts. To gain a thorough understanding of the concepts presented, the reader is referred to the bibliography.

Accounting systems

An accounting system is a formal means of gathering and communicating financial data. It is used to assist and inform collective decision-making to help achieve organizational objectives. An effective system provides information for such purposes as

- internal reporting to managers for use in
- o planning and controlling routine operations
- o making special decisions and formulating strategies
- external reporting to shareholders, government, and other outside parties, for use in shareholder investment decisions, tax calculations and a variety of other applications.

Management (internal parties) and external parties share an interest in these purposes but, as Table 2.1 shows, financial accounting and management accounting differ. Financial

11

Table 2.1. Management and financial accounting compared

	Management accounting	Financial accounting
1. Primary users	Organization managers at various levels.	Outside parties such as shareholders, creditors and government agencies, but also organization managers.
2. Freedom of choice	No constraints other than costs in relation to benefits of improved management decisions.	Constrained by company law and accounting standards.
3. Behavioural implications	The effect of measurements and reports on manager's daily behaviour and therefore on the future financial performance of the company.	The impact of financial information on outside parties.
4. Time focus	Forward looking: formal use of budgets as well as historical records e.g. 1989 actual against 1989 budget.	Past orientation: historical evaluation, e.g. 1989 actual against 1988 actual performance.
5. Time span	Flexible, varying from hourly to ten or 15 years.	Less flexible: usually one year or one quarter.
6. Reports	Detailed reports, for example on subsidiaries or divisions, products, departments and geographical areas.	Summary reports, concerned primarily with the whole entity.
7. Delineation of activities	Field is less sharply defined. Heavier use of economics, decision sciences, and behavioural sciences.	Field is more sharply defined. Less use of related disciplines.

accounting has traditionally focused on the historical, stewardship aspects of external reporting, whereas management accounting involves the preparation, interpretation and communication of information to assist executives in fulfilling organizational objectives.

Financial statements

Managers, investors and other interested groups invariably wish to know how well an organization performed during a given period and its financial position at a given point in time. An accountant answers these questions with two financial statements: a profit and loss account and a balance sheet. A profit and loss account (an example of which is shown in Fig. 2.1) includes revenues and expenses relevant to an accounting period (usually one year) and shows the resulting profit or loss. A balance sheet (an example of which is shown in Fig. 2.2), or statement of financial position, shows the assets owned or controlled at the date of the balance sheet and how they are financed.

In addition, a source and application of funds statement (an example of which is shown in Fig. 2.3) is usually produced to show the various sources of funds received during the period in question and how those funds have been spent. This statement is drawn up from information contained in the profit and loss account, the balance sheet, and notes on accounts which accompany full, published accounts. These notes amplify information contained in the statements. They have not been included in the examples given in Figs 2.1 and 2.2. For this reason the reader should resist the temptation to follow the figures given in the examples through to the source and application of funds statement in Fig. 2.3, which is presented for illustrative purposes only. The relationship between this statement and the two other main statements is shown in Fig. 2.4. The balance sheet provides a 'static picture' of the financial position at a point in time; the profit and loss account and source and application of funds statement show the flows which have occurred during the accounting period.

The following analogy may prove helpful in understanding these statements. Consider an engineer running a water storage and distribution company. He has gauges recording the depth and hence volume of water stored in every reservoir. He also has meters on the pipes connecting the reservoirs to the distribution system, and flow gauges on every stream, which measure flow and hence volume passing during any past period.

The reservoir depth gauges, at any instant, would tell the engineer how much water is in the system and where it is. These measurements correspond to items on a balance sheet. The flow

Bloggshire plc: profit and loss account for year ended 31 December 1988

	£ million
Sales	480
Cost of sales	(340)
Gross profit	140
Operating expenses	(104)
Operating profit	36
Other revenues	—
Other expenses	(4)
Profit on ordinary activities before taxation and exceptional item(s)	32
Exceptional item(s)	—
Profit on ordinary activities before taxation	32
Tax on profit on ordinary activities	(14)
Profit on ordinary activities after taxation	18
Extraordinary item(s)	—
Profit attributable to shareholders	18
Dividends	(10)
Profit retained for the year	8

Notes on terms used in the profit and loss account

1. *Profit and loss account*. This financial statement summarizes the revenues and expenses of a business for a period and shows the overall profit or loss. It also shows the extent to which profits of the current period are paid out as dividends or retained in the business.
2. *Cost of sales*. Stocks at the beginning of the year plus purchases during the year minus stocks at the end of the year.
3. *Operating expenses* include wages, rent, rates, depreciation, research and development expenditure.
4. *Other revenues* include rent and loan interest receivable.
5. *Other expenses* include loan interest payable.
6. *Exceptional items* are those arising from the ordinary activities of a business which need to be disclosed separately because of their unusual nature or size (for example, profits or losses on the disposal of fixed assets).
7. *Extraordinary items* are those arising from events or transactions outside the ordinary activities of a business which are not expected to occur frequently or regularly (for example, the financial effects of the discontinuation of a significant part of the business).
8. *Dividends* represent the amount of profit distributed or proposed to be distributed to the owners of the share capital (i.e. the shareholders).

Fig. 2.1.   Example of a profit and loss account; the brackets around amounts within the profit and loss account indicate a deduction on outgoings

meter measurements tell the engineer how much water has moved where over a period of time. These measurements correspond to items on a profit and loss account.

This analogy could be extended to the source and application of funds statement. Sources and applications of funds could be represented by decreases and increases in reservoir volume, respectively. However, the situation is slightly more complex in this case because some items (for example, depreciation and revaluation of fixed assets) do not involve movement of funds. These items could be represented by twin reservoirs for which only the net flow relative to the remainder of the system would be measured. An example of this would be the value of a piece of equipment where its gross book value would be represented by the total volume of water in the two reservoirs. One reservoir would represent total depreciation, the other the net book value of the equipment (that is, gross value less total depreciation).

Practice of accounting

To prepare these financial statements accountants must break into the records of a continuous stream of transactions (i.e. events which affect the financial position of a business) at regular intervals to

- identify and measure the revenues and expenses relating to an accounting period
- identify and measure the assets held (including those relating to incomplete transactions) and summarize the sources of finance which are the external liabilities of the business and the interests of the owners
- compare the assets and liabilities at the beginning and end of an accounting period to determine where funds have come from and how they have been invested.

Accounting is not a simple task. Usually results can only approximate to some 'ideal' measure. Some items of revenue and expense may be easy to assign to specific accounting periods but incomplete transactions raise problems. For example, accountants need to decide in which period to charge costs intended to generate future benefits. They must also identify and attach a definite value at the balance sheet date to assets, liabilities, unsold stocks and partly used equipment. Problems of this kind do not yield uniquely

Bloggshire plc: balance sheet as at 31 December 1988

	1988 £ million	1987 £ million
Fixed assets		
Tangible assets	160	140
Investments	—	—
	160	140
Current assets		
Stock	80	50
Debtors	70	60
Cash	30	20
	180	130
Current liabilities		
Creditors: amounts falling due within one year		
Bank and other loans	36	24
Dividend	10	4
Corporation tax	14	10
	60	38
Net current assets	120	92
Total assets less current liabilities	280	232
Creditors: amounts falling due after more than one year		
Bank and other loans	40	30
Provisions for liabilities and charges	—	—
	240	202
Share capital and reserves		
Share capital	200	170
Share premium account	—	—
Revaluation reserve	—	—
Profit and loss account	40	32
	240	202

Fig. 2.2. Example of a balance sheet

'correct' solutions. They depend on assumptions which have been made and on uncertain future events. Thus measurement often involves the exercise of judgement.

Fundamental accounting concepts and terminology

Accountants have devised a number of broad assumptions which are widely accepted in preparing published accounts. The more important of these assumptions will be dealt with here.

Accounting usually focuses on measurement of the financial

Notes on terms used in the balance sheet

1. A *Balance sheet* is a financial statement summarizing the assets and liabilities of a business (on a particular date) and how the net assets have been financed.
2. *Assets* are economic resources (for example, cash, stock and equipment) which are expected to benefit future cash inflows or to help reduce future outflows.
3. *Liabilities* are economic obligations owed to others (such as debt owed to a bank or an amount payable resulting from the purchase of goods or services on credit).
4. *Shareholders' funds* are amounts of money which ultimately belong to the shareholders. They are not liabilities in the same sense as other sources of funds, as they are not normally payable to the shareholders unless

   - the business ceases to exist, or
   - the directors decide to pay dividends out of past retained earnings.

   Shareholders' funds (otherwise known as owners' equity) exist in the form of issued capital, retained profits, or other reserves. Shareholders' funds represent the balance of an organization's assets less its liabilities. These funds thus represent a residual amount, depending on the profits generated and the book value attached to the assets of the business.
5. *Fixed assets* are resources (both tangible, such as land and buildings, plant and machinery and intangible such as franchises, patents, trademarks, copyrights) with a relatively long economic life, which are acquired for use in producing other goods and services, but not for resale in the ordinary course of business.
6. *Current liabilities* are liabilities due to be paid within one year from the date of the balance sheet such as trade creditors, proposed dividends and current tax liabilities.
7. *Current assets* are represented either by cash or assets which are expected to be converted into cash, consumed by the business within one year from the date of the balance sheet, such as stocks, debtors and prepaid expenses.
8. *Net current assets (or working capital)* is the excess of current assets over current liabilities. This represents the circulating capital of the business.
9. *Provisions for liabilities and charges* include deferred taxation.
10. *Share capital* represents the total nominal (or face) value of the shares issued by the company.
11. *Share premium account* arises when shares are issued at a price greater than their nominal value.
12. *Revaluation reserve.* When fixed assets are revalued, any surplus over book value is incorporated in the accounts by showing the fixed assets at the new higher figure and including the surplus as a capital reserve.
13. *Profit and loss account* represents the cumulative after-tax profit (less any losses) made by a business since its formation which has not been distributed to shareholders in the form of dividends.

impact of events as they affect a particular business entity such as a sole proprietorship, a partnership or a company. A sole proprietorship is a separate organization with a single owner, such as small shops and professional businesses. A partnership is an unincorporated body of people combined for a common business objective. Unlike a company, a partnership does not exist as a separate legal entity: for example, a partnership cannot sue and be sued in its own right. It is owned by the partners in common and each partner (except a limited partner) is liable for the debts

17

Bloggshire plc: source and application of funds statement for the year ended 31 December 1988

	£ million
Source of funds	
Profit before taxation	32
Extraordinary item(s)	—
	32
Adjustments for certain items not involving the movement of funds	
Depreciation on tangible assets	10
Revaluation surplus realized in the year	—
Funds generated from operations	42
Funds from other sources	
Disposal of fixed assets	—
Total source of funds	42
Application of funds	
Dividends paid	4
Taxation paid	10
Capital expenditure	
On tangible assets	30
On investments	—
Change in working capital	
Stocks increase	30
Debtors increase	10
Decrease in creditors due within one year	(12)
Total application of funds	72
Net cash inflow/(outflow)	(30)
Financed by	
Issues of shares	30
Increase in borrowing	10
	40
Net increase in cash balance	10

Fig. 2.3. Example of a source and application of funds statement; a source and application of funds statement can be compiled by determining the changes in the balance sheet figures during the year: see Fig. 2.2 and by referring to the profit and loss account

of the firm. A company is a legal entity whose affairs are mainly regulated by the Companies Act 1985. It may be limited by shares or by guarantee, or it may be unlimited. The great majority of companies in the construction industry are companies limited by shares, to which this chapter refers. The dominant characteristic

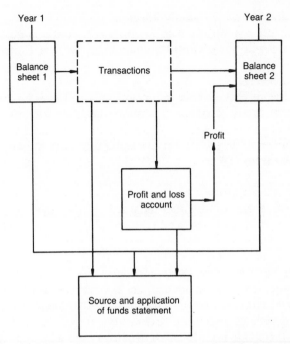

Fig. 2.4. Relationship between main financial statements showing information flows

of a limited share company is that it exists as a separate legal entity which is distinct from its shareholders (the members). The assets and debts belong to the company which continues to exist until it is dissolved. Under the Companies Act 1985 there are two kinds of company limited by shares: public and private companies. Private companies, which comprise the great majority of registered companies, are frequently family businesses. The number of members in a private company is limited and there are limitations on the transfer of shares. Membership of a public company is unlimited and shares, which are quoted on the Stock Exchange, are freely transferable. Both private and public companies are required by the Companies Act 1985 to file annual financial accounts which are available for public inspection. The consequences of this requirement are examined in the next chapter.

Four fundamental accounting concepts will now be considered.

19

Continuity (the going concern concept)

This is an assumption that an entity will continue indefinitely or at least will not go into liquidation in the near future.

Accruals concept

This means that revenue is recognized as services are rendered and expenses are recognized as efforts are expended or services used to obtain the revenue, regardless of when cash is received or disbursed. The section on matching discusses the application of this concept.

Concept of consistency

The same accounting methods are applied over a series of reporting periods so that trends can be identified and comparisons made.

Conservatism (the concept of prudence)

Revenues are not included in an income statement until they are realized either in cash or in the form of other assets, the ultimate cash proceeds of which are reasonably certain. In contrast, full provision is made for all known expenses even where the amount has to be estimated.

Accounting terms

The following terms are frequently used by accountants.

Materiality

A transaction is material if a user of the financial statements under consideration would tend to be misled by its omission or mis-statement.

Matching

Linking revenues with the expenses incurred in achieving them is referred to as matching. Revenues realized in a particular period (measured by the selling prices of goods and services delivered to customers) less related expenses (measured by the cost of goods and services used) gives a profit for the period in question.

Some expenses may cause problems of allocation between accounting periods such as research and development expenditure. In general, the future benefits of most research projects are too uncertain to justify carrying the expenditure forward. The expenditure concerned therefore will be written off in the year in which it is incurred. However, if there is a clearly defined project, the related expenditure is clearly identifiable, and if there is a reasonable expectation of sufficient future benefits at least to cover all the costs, development expenditure may be carried forward as an asset on the balance sheet and amortized over the period(s) expected to benefit.

Accounting bases

Accounting bases are methods of applying fundamental concepts to deal with the increasing variety of business transactions. Accounting bases aim to provide consistent, fair and objective methods to deal with problems such as depreciation of fixed assets, valuing stock, translation of foreign currencies and inflation. Businesses have become so complex and diverse that it is not possible to achieve complete uniformity of accounting bases.

Accounting policies

Accounting policies are the specific bases which an enterprise chooses and follows consistently as being, in the opinion of management, best suited to present its financial results fairly. To enable readers to understand its financial statements properly, a company must disclose its accounting policies. Preparation of financial statements by companies registered in the UK is guided by the Generally Accepted Accounting Practice (GAAP) which is set out in Statements of Standard Accounting Practice (SSAPs) and in Statements of Recommended Practice (SORPs). Companies must comply with GAAP.

SSAPs and SORPs are developed by the Accounting Standards Committee of the Consultative Committee of Accountancy Bodies (CCAB) and are issued by the governing bodies of the accountancy profession. SSAPs and SORPs are authoritative statements on best accounting practice that aim to narrow the areas of difference and variety in the accounting treatment of the matters with which they deal. Unlike SSAPs, SORPs are not mandatory but companies are encouraged to comply with the recommendations that they make. In addition to SSAPs and SORPs, each professional body issues, from time to time, other statements on accounting matters that form part of GAAP.

21

Analysing business accounts

The structure of the main financial statements has been described: the profit and loss account (Fig. 2.1), the balance sheet (Fig. 2.2) and source and application of funds statement (Fig. 2.3). Accounts as a whole will now be looked at and how to extract the most useful information for assessing performance and financial position will be considered. For convenience company accounts are examined but similar considerations would apply to other business entities.

The information disclosed in published accounts may relate to a single company or to a group of companies under a holding company. It will indicate

- the different kinds of assets and how they are financed
- the relationship between debt and shareholders' funds and between current assets and liabilities
- the level of sales and profit
- earnings per share and dividends.

Analysis of financial statements can be broken down into four major steps.

Overview analysis

To place a detailed analysis in context it is necessary to look at trends in key figures over a number of years and to make comparisons with other firms in the same industry. The figures selected will obviously depend on the nature of a company's business, but generally the most interesting trends to note will include: sales, net assets, profit, and dividends.

Ratio analysis

Ratios are computed from published financial statements. Evaluation of a financial ratio requires a comparison. There are three main types of comparisons: first, with historical ratios of the company in question (called time-series comparisons); second, with figures based on experience; and third, with ratios of other companies or with industry averages (called cross-sectional comparisons). When approaching a detailed ratio analysis of a company's accounts it is helpful to group the ratios under three main headings to measure different aspects of the company's activities.

- *Performance ratios* attempt to answer the question: how well is the business being run? They include ratios measuring return on investment (both on ordinary shareholders' funds and on the total net assets employed), margins on sales and measures of stock holdings and trade credit extended.

- *Financial status ratios* indicate the financial position of the company and distinguish between solvency (that is, the ability of a company to meet its financial obligations as they become due) and liquidity (that is, the ability of a company to meet its short-term liabilities), and between long-term and short-term capacity to meet liabilities.

- *Stock market ratios* relate financial results to the number of shares issued and to stock market prices. They include earnings per share, dividend yield and other measures. A list of ratios is set out in Table 2.2.

Analysis of business segments

Where a company is engaged in more than one kind of business, it is not unusual for significant differences to arise from year to year between the separate segments. Indeed this is sometimes thought to be one of the justifications for diversification. Thus looking at changes in sales in the various business segments is important when analysing overall profit margin. Where the results of some parts of the total business are improving and others are declining, the total figure may be an inadequate reflection of what is actually happening. In particular, the aggregate results may show less fluctuation over time than the results of some of the separate segments of the business. Where possible the analyst must identify and investigate detailed results. This will be especially important where significant acquisitions or disposals have occurred.

Source and application of funds analysis

The main sources and applications of funds can be identified and any changes over time recorded.

Major elements of financial accounting

The aspects of accounting introduced here are discussed briefly so that the reader will gain an elementary understanding of them.

Table 2.2. Financial ratios

Category	Name of ratio	Numerator	Denominator	Measure
Performance	Return on equity: %	Profit after tax	Ordinary shareholders' funds	Efficiency with which shareholders' equity is being employed within the firm
	Return on net assets: %	Profit before interest and tax	Total assets less current liabilities	Efficiency with which capital is employed within the firm
	Profit margin: %	Profit before interest and tax	Sales	Profitability
	Net asset turnover	Sales	Total assets less current liabilities	Operating performance
	Stock turnover	Cost of sales	Stock	Speed of selling inventory
	Debtors' ratio: days	Debtors × 365	Sales	Average length of time that debtors are outstanding

	Ratio			
Financial status	Debt ratio: %	Long-term debt	Total assets less current liabilities	Capital structure (i.e. proportions of debt and equity financing)
	Interest cover	Profit before interest and tax	Loan interest	Ability to meet loan interest obligations
	Current ratio	Current assets	Current liabilities	Adequacy of working capital
	Acid test	Liquid assets (debtors and cash)	Current liabilities	Liquidity
Stock market	Earnings per share	Profit after tax	Number of ordinary shares issued	
	Price/earnings ratio	Market price per share	Earnings per share	Capital market performance
	Dividend yield: %	Dividend per share (net)	Market per price share	
	Dividend cover	Profit (earnings) per share	Dividend per share	

For those who wish to pursue these procedures in greater depth, the bibliography at the end of this guide should be consulted.

Double-entry book-keeping

This system is so named because at least two accounts (for example, cash, stock, accounts payable) are always affected by each transaction. Transactions and books must always balance.

Depreciation

Depreciation is the process of allocation of the difference between the total acquisition cost of an asset (or its valuation) and its estimated residual value (i.e. predicted disposal value at the end of its useful life) over the total useful life of the asset. The depreciation allocation to each year may be made on the basis of time or service using one of a variety of methods (for example, straight line, units of production, sum of the years' digits, reducing balance) which are described in most standard accounting texts.

Equity method for inter-corporate investments

Investments in the shares of one company by another company are accounted for in different ways, depending on the type of relationship between the investor and the investee.

The equity method is generally used for a holding of 20–50% of the outstanding voting shares (that is, shares which have been issued and which are currently held by shareholders) because it is assumed, on the basis of this level of ownership, that an investor has the ability to exert significant influence in the affairs of the company. The equity method accounts for the investment at acquisition cost, adjusted for the investor's share of dividends and earnings, or losses of the investee, after the date of investment. Accordingly, the value of the investment recorded on the balance sheet is increased by the investor's share of the investee's earnings. This amount is reduced by dividends received from the investee and by the investor's share of investee's losses.

The cost method is generally used to account for interests of less than 20%. The initial investment is recorded at cost and dividends are recorded as income when received. However, the determining factor in each case is the extent of the investor's influence over the investee in the financial and operating policy decisions of a company. For example, partners in a joint venture or consortium may hold interests of less than 20% separately, but greater than 20% collectively.

Consolidated financial statements

A publicly held business is typically composed of two or more separate legal entities which constitute a single overall economic unit. This is almost always a parent-subsidiary relationship where one company (the parent) owns more than 50% of the outstanding voting shares of another company (the subsidiary).

Companies having a controlling interest (i.e. greater than 50% interest) in other companies are required to issue consolidated financial statements. Consolidated statements combine the financial positions and earnings reports of the parent company with those of various subsidiaries into an overall report as if they were a single entity. The aim is to give the readers a better perspective than could be obtained by examining a large number of separate reports of individual companies.

Corporate taxation

Taxation is a complex and rapidly changing subject. It is discussed only briefly here. Readers are referred to the bibliography for further sources of information on this subject. Corporate taxation includes corporation tax on profits and capital gains, value added tax (VAT) and advance corporation tax (ACT) on dividends. These taxes are discussed in general terms here. Their relevance to project appraisal is considered in chapter 5.

Corporation tax on profits and advance corporation tax on dividends

In computing the amount of a company's annual profits subject to corporation tax, certain adjustments are required to be made to the profit before tax reported in published accounts. These would include adjustment for items which are not tax deductible; for example entertaining, and items for which special reliefs are given; for example capital expenditure where allowances at certain specified rates can be claimed instead of depreciation as shown in the accounts.

Profits earned overseas by companies registered in the UK may be subject to overseas taxation, but corporation tax on those profits is usually reduced by overseas taxation suffered; in effect, overseas profits are usually subject to UK corporation tax only to the extent

27

that the rate of overseas tax is lower than the UK rate (double tax relief).

Corporation tax is generally payable nine months after the end of a company's financial year. However, an advance payment, called ACT, is due whenever a company pays dividends to its shareholders. ACT may be offset against past, present and future payments of corporation tax within certain specified limits.

Losses are computed in a similar way to profits. For tax purposes, losses may be carried forward and, subject to certain restrictions, set against future profits or they may be relieved against profits elsewhere in a group of companies. They may also be carried back one year in most circumstances.

Sole traders and partnerships are liable to income tax on business profits, rather than corporation tax. Taxable profits, which are calculated in a similar way to companies' taxable profits, are treated as personal income to the sole trader, or split between partners in proportion to their share of profits in the year of assessment. Losses incurred by sole traders or partnerships can be set against other income in that fiscal year, or carried back for up to three fiscal years depending on the circumstances. Unrelieved losses may also be carried forward and, subject to certain restrictions, set against future profits.

Corporation tax on capital gains

The capital gain or loss calculated for corporation tax purposes on the disposal of property, plant, equipment or other assets is usually measured as the difference between the sale price and the base cost of the asset plus a deduction for indexation (an allowance given for the effects of inflation during the period of ownership of the asset). The base cost is usually the original cost, but in certain circumstances the market value at 6 April 1965 or 31 March 1982 can be used instead. Unlike trading losses, no mechanism exists for carry back or surrender of capital losses to other group companies, and they can only be carried forward for use by the same company.

When proceeds from the disposal of business assets are reinvested in certain other business assets the chargeable gain arising can be deferred. Where the new asset(s) are depreciating assets such as fixed plant and machinery, the deferral is for a maximum of ten years. The deferral is indefinite if reinvestment is in nondepreciating assets such as freehold land and buildings. This 'rollover' relief makes the proceeds of many business fixed asset disposals tax-free as long as replacement continues.

VAT

For the purpose of assessing liability to VAT in the UK, supplies of goods or services provided by a business are divided into taxable supplies (standard-rated supplies liable to VAT at the standard rate and zero-rated supplies) and exempt supplies. If all of the supplies made by a business are taxable, it is allowed to reclaim from Customs and Excise all VAT incurred on most of its supplies (input VAT). If a business makes both exempt and taxable supplies, it is said to be partially exempt and will be able to recover only part of the input VAT. Partially exempt enterprises include banks and insurance companies. Businesses, such as property investment companies, which may make wholly exempt supplies, cannot reclaim any input VAT.

Deferred tax

Deferred tax arises as the result of the accounting concept of accruals (discussed earlier in chapter 2). This works to smooth the effect of the different treatment of certain items of income and expenditure for corporation tax and accounting purposes. Provision for deferred tax is only made for any differences when they are expected to reverse in the foreseeable future, and no provision is usually made for deferred tax assets.

For example, over the life of an asset, both capital allowances and company depreciation will generally amount to original cost less ultimate sales proceeds, but the pattern over time may be different. Capital allowances deducted from the taxable income may be higher in the early years (and therefore lower in the later years) than book depreciation, which may be charged over a longer period. Hence in the early years of the life of a fixed asset the taxable profit may be less than the reported profit before tax. A deferred tax charge in the profit and loss account would reflect the difference between the actual tax charge and the tax liability which would be incurred if the company's own depreciation charge were deductible for tax purposes. In later years, when book depreciation exceeds capital allowances, this deferred tax can be credited to the profit and loss account to smooth the effect over time.

Current cost accounting

The basic objective of current cost accounting is to provide more useful information than is available from historical cost accounts alone for the guidance of management, shareholders and others on such matters as

- the financial viability of a business
- return on investment
- pricing policy and cost control.

A change in input prices of goods and services used and financed by the business will affect the amount of funds required to maintain the operating capability of the net operating assets, i.e. fixed assets, stock and monetary working capital. Changes in the values of net operating assets are reflected in a current cost reserve (revaluation reserve) in the balance sheet. Further, to the extent that assets have been used to earn revenue, the difference between the historical cost and the current cost of resources used up is shown as an expense in the profit and loss account. Current cost accounting is particularly important during periods of high inflation. However, this method is currently little used in the UK.

Foreign currency transactions

Many large companies acquire overseas subsidiaries and others build up their overseas interests internally from retained earnings and local borrowings. As a result, a number of multi-national companies have emerged which control a large number of foreign subsidiaries.

For the purposes of consolidation, the accounts of foreign subsidiaries operating abroad have to be translated into terms of the domestic currency of the holding company. The method used to translate the financial statements should reflect the financial and other operational relationships which exist between an investing company and its foreign enterprises (refer to SSAP 20). Foreign transactions may be seen as parts of a single world-wide system where individual entries should be translated into the holding company's currency as they arise (the temporal method). Alternatively, they may be seen as relating to foreign investments which should be translated at the year-end (the closing rate method). The essential difference between these methods arises because the exchange rate between the local currency and the domestic currency of the holding company may have changed between the two dates.

Management accounting

Management process and accounting

As outlined in chapter 1, the management process is primarily concerned with decision-making, that is choosing a course of action from a set of possible courses of action in the light of agreed objectives. These decisions range from the routine (for example, preparing daily work schedules) to the non-routine, such as beginning a new contract. Decision-making underlies the commonly encountered division of the management process into planning and control.

Planning means deciding objectives and the means for achieving them. Controlling covers implementation of plans and the use of feedback so that objectives are attained. A 'feedback loop' is the central means of control and timely, systematic measurement is the chief means of providing useful feedback. Planning and controlling are so intertwined that it is artificial to draw rigid lines between them.

Accounting formalizes plans by expressing them quantitatively as budgets. Control is formalized for accounting purposes as performance reports which provide feedback by comparing results with plans and by highlighting variances (that is, deviations from budgets).

The concentration of a manager's attention and effort on significant deviations from expected results is known as management by exception. The management information system should indicate what is most in need of investigation. Managers should not ordinarily be concerned with results which conform closely with plans. However well-conceived, plans should incorporate sufficient flexibility so that a manager may feel free to pursue opportunities which may arise after a budget has been settled. Management by exception enables a manager to devote his or her energies to significant deviations; this does not mean that he or she ignores all other results but it helps to focus managerial effort. In other words, managers should not cling blindly to a plan when unfolding events indicate the desirability of actions which were not originally authorized. Nevertheless, there is always a need to examine variances from budget to identify those which could be controlled and thus require management action. Variances may often reveal weaknesses in control systems which should be rectified.

An essential tool in management accounting is the budget. A budget should be built up from first principles, to identify the component tasks, the resources which are needed to carry out these tasks and to enable the required resources to be costed. The phasing of expenditure within the budget should also be determined.

This process is analogous to estimating, programming and monitoring a construction project. For example, each activity on a construction programme is priced by estimators and its timing is reflected in the sequencing of the activities forming the construction bar chart or network. The preparation of a budget provides a measure against which actual performance can be monitored. It also provides essential data for identifying weaknesses and potential improvements in performance (as does a construction programme which is carefully monitored).

Differences between the actual costs and cost profile and the budget are called variances. Variances may relate to cost or volume of work, that is controllable items, but not to inflation. For example, if the quantity of sheet piling was increased in a temporary works item a variance would be identified between the budget and actual costs. A variance should prompt questions which identify areas in which cost and project control may be improved. For example, were the quantities of sheet piling increased because ground conditions were worse than expected? Was the job underestimated? Has there been exceptional wastage? Has sheet piling been transferred between sites without materials transferred and received records being produced? Reconciliation of the actual costs and the budget should be done regularly throughout the relevant budget period.

Uncontrollable items, such as inflation, are best treated separately from controllable costs so that cause and effect can be related more readily and to avoid unnecessary worrying about items over which the budget-holder has no influence.

Other uncontrollable and indirect costs might include office overhead costs or costs attributable to a change in the working rule agreement for construction employees. The fact that costs are uncontrollable does not necessarily mean that the budget-holder would not be asked to find savings to cover uncontrollable increases.

The process of reconciliation of budget costs and actual costs provides invaluable data so that standardized costs may be developed and used on comparable activities and projects in the future. This is particularly useful for repetitive tasks such as kerb-laying, more complex activities such as the fitting out of aeration tanks for a sewage treatment works or even in the design office for the production of reinforcement drawings or outline design drawings.

The level of detail within a budget should be related to the responsibilities of the budget-holders and the nature of the task so that it provides a mechanism for control. For example, a project engineer might estimate how many drawings would be necessary to describe the works to be constructed and may well find that cost increments of £1000 are significant in controlling drawing production. The partner in charge of several project engineers, however, will be looking at a coarser level of cost increment (say £5000) in controlling and monitoring the performance of his or her group of engineers.

Data collected in budget preparation and monitoring are an invaluable input to a management information system which may be used to analyse trends within or between projects or perhaps between design groups in an engineering consultancy.

3 Audit

This chapter explains the nature and purpose of an audit, outlines the main features of an audit report, compares and contrasts internal and external auditing and describes a particular type of audit called a contract audit.

Background

The Auditing Standards and Guidelines, which are developed by the Auditing Practices Committee (a committee of the Consultative Committee of Accountancy Bodies), prescribe the principles and practices which members of the relevant accountancy bodies in the UK are expected to follow in the conduct of an audit. They are analogous to SSAPs. The foreword to the Auditing Standards and Guidelines describes an audit in the following broad terms

> An audit is the independent examination and expression of opinion on the financial statements of an enterprise by an appointed auditor in pursuance of that appointment and in compliance with any relevant statutory obligation.

It should be noted that this definition covers the audit of any enterprise, not just that of a limited company. For convenience, however, auditing shall be described with reference to the requirements of companies.

There are three main types of audit. In the case of a company, for example, independent auditors report to the shareholders their opinion on the truth and fairness of published financial statements. This is known as an external audit. An audit may also take the form of an investigation of the internal systems of control (carried out by internal auditors, who are employed by an organization).

This is known as an internal audit. The third type of audit is a particular kind of investigation, such as a contract audit, which is performed by specialist auditors and consultants.

The role of auditors can be traced back many hundreds of years. In medieval times independent auditors were employed by feudal barons to ensure that returns from tenant farmers accurately reflected revenues received from estates. The development of auditing accompanied the growth of the company as a separate legal entity. This led to the separation of ownership from management and the need to safeguard the interests of the owners (the shareholders) who were not involved in the day to day affairs of running the business. In the nineteenth century, the services of professional accountants were increasingly sought. A series of important enactments more recently has confirmed and strengthened the position of auditors. The Companies Act 1948 required auditors to express an opinion on the profit and loss account as well as the balance sheet. The Companies Act 1948 and subsequent enactments were consolidated by the Companies Act 1985 to which reference should be made by those readers who wish to gain a more detailed understanding of the legal basis of auditing.

Audit objectives

The first objective of a company audit is to express an expert and independent opinion on the truth and fairness of information contained in the balance sheet and the profit and loss account: see section 236 of the Companies Act 1985. The bases and policies used by the audit should be generally acceptable both to the accountancy profession and to the business community. They should also be appropriate to the nature and circumstances of the business in question and applied consistently from year to year.

The second main objective of an audit is to ascertain and evaluate the reliability of the accounting systems used as the basis for preparation of the financial statements. The aim of verifying the accuracy and reliability of records and documents (by examination and testing) is to obtain support for the expression of an opinion on the financial statements. The auditor must therefore judge the suitability of the systems and the data produced as the basis for evaluating accounting information. It should be noted that owing to the increase in size and complexity of modern business, the development of computer systems and the requirement that an auditor should review transactions over a period to report on the profit and loss account, the modern practice of auditing has moved away from a detailed checking of a mass of individual items towards a review of the systems in operation.

Auditors should also consider the possibility of fraud and other irregularities and their effect on the truth and fairness of the view given in the financial statements. Auditors are not responsible for detecting every item of fraud and error. Rather, they are responsible for using reasonable care and skill as is appropriate in the circumstances to prevent the occurrence of fraud and error. In this respect the role of an auditor may be likened to that of a watchdog rather than a bloodhound.

Auditors may also provide advice to a client with the accounts, in the form of a management letter, using their knowledge of the client's affairs and their own experience to give recommendations on the systems of internal control and on the efficiency of the accounting system, as well as advice on such matters as tax planning.

Audit report

Auditors normally issue a report which is a statement used as a preface to the financial statements of a company. To comply with the Companies Act 1985, auditors are required (by section 236) to state expressly whether, in their opinion, the balance sheet and the profit and loss account (and, if it is a holding company submitting group accounts, the group accounts) have been properly prepared in accordance with the statutory requirements, and whether the accounts show a 'true and fair view' of the state of the company's affairs and of its profit (or loss). It should be noted that an audit report is an opinion based on an independent examination of available evidence. It is not a warranty of the facts contained in the financial statements.

In preparing their report, the auditors are required (by section 237) to carry out such investigations as will enable them to form an opinion as to whether proper accounting records have been kept by the company and whether the company's balance sheet and (if not consolidated) its profit and loss account are in agreement with the accounting records and returns. For this purpose auditors are entitled, under section 237(3), to inspect the company's books and to require from the company's officers such information as they think necessary for the performance of their duties.

In addition to the statutory requirements, the form and content of an audit report is governed by requirements laid down in auditing standards. These require an explicit opinion or statement as to whether or not the source and application of funds statement gives a true and fair view and what accounting convention (historical or current cost) has been adopted for the presentation of the accounts. Stock Exchange requirements and all relevant SSAPs will also need to have been complied with.

The different categories of audit report are summarized in Table 3.1. When auditors give qualified reports, they should refer to all material matters about which they have reservations, giving their reasons in each case together with a quantification of its effect on the financial statements if this is both relevant and practicable. A matter is 'material' if knowledge of the matter would be likely to influence the user of the financial statements. A qualified audit report, as opposed to an unqualified report, should leave the reader in no doubt as to its meaning and implications. Qualifications to audit reports may be classified as given in Table 3.2.

Table 3.1. Categories of audit report

Auditors' opinion	Comment
Unqualified	The auditors have no material reservations about the financial statements and accounting records from which they have been prepared.
Qualified	An expression of dissatisfaction about the financial statements and/or accounting records. Reservations must be material.
Uncertainty	Major matters within GAAP.
Adverse	Financial statements are not within GAAP; do not give a true and fair view.
Disclaimer	Auditors unable to express an opinion as to whether financial statements give a true and fair view.

Table 3.2. Qualifications to audit reports

Nature of qualification	Material but not fundamental	Fundamental
Uncertainty	'Subject to' opinion	Disclaim opinion
Disagreement	'Except' opinion	Adverse opinion

Uncertainty may arise because of lack of proper accounting records or the outcome of litigation, for example. Disagreement may arise from failure to agree facts or amounts included in the accounts. As an auditor will qualify his or her report only in relation to a material matter, the reader of the accounts should consider the matter seriously. Before expressing a qualified opinion an auditor should always try to resolve problems with the management of the organization concerned.

External and internal auditing
In the case of a company, external auditors are appointed by the members (shareholders). In practice they are recommended for appointment by the board of directors. The primary task of the external auditors is to report on the truth and fairness of the financial statements which are presented to the members at their annual general meeting. An external auditor will need to carry out detailed checking of records and procedures. The auditor's work on systems of internal control is a subsidiary task.

Internal auditors are appointed by the directors. Their responsibility is to the management of the firm and their task is to assess the internal control systems of the organization. An internal system of control of a business should be designed to ensure that the policies of the management are being followed, that financial records are accurate, that the assets of the company have been safeguarded and that the opportunities for fraud are kept to a minimum. The level of internal control required would depend on the nature, size and volume of transactions, the degree of control which management are able to exercise themselves and the organizational structure. Internal auditors will review the accounting systems and related controls, examine the financial and operating information needed for management (including detailed tests of transactions and balances), assess the efficiency and effectiveness of controls and review the implementation of corporate objectives. Internal auditors may also carry out special assignments on behalf of the management, looking at a wide range of business matters.

The scope of an internal auditor's work is determined by the management. An external auditor must decide the scope of the work to be undertaken to discharge his or her duties. In this connection an external auditor will wish to consider what reliance should be placed on an internal audit. In large organizations it has become common practice for audit committees, consisting of representatives of senior management, the internal audit department and external auditors, to meet. Non-executive directors are often invited to participate in these meetings as representatives of the shareholders. Audit committee meetings enable internal and external auditors to discuss their findings with senior management and provide the latter with an opportunity to express their concerns to the auditors.

Contract audit

A contract audit is a particular type of audit. It does not replace the need for an internal audit of a major construction project. If properly performed, a contract audit provides an opportunity to assess the management and control of a contract, especially if the process begins during the pre-construction and early construction stages and extends to a post-completion review and verification. It can identify weaknesses in systems and procedures. A contract audit may also serve to reassure a client who is unfamiliar with construction that the project is being carried out efficiently and effectively.

A contract audit is usually performed by a multi-disciplinary team embracing construction professionals and auditors; the latter may be specialist internal auditors or a firm of external auditors. Their task is not simply to carry out a paperwork exercise. Apart from validating the contracts, overall project management arrangements and systems and procedures against available documentation, it is often necessary for the team to make site visits and carry out inspections of goods and materials belonging to the client which are held off site.

Objectives of contract audit

The objectives of a contract audit are determined by the nature and circumstances of a particular contract. In general terms, the objectives will be

- to evaluate the adequacy of systems to control time, cost and quality
- to evaluate the timeliness and relevance of management information
- to relate any potential losses owing to poor control on site or systems abuse and, where specific losses are identified, to determine whether fraud has occurred
- to assess compliance with internal procedures (for example, standing orders or standing financial instructions in a public sector organization).

Approach

An approach to a contract audit is represented in the flowchart in Fig. 3.1. This approach consists of three principal phases (systems evaluation, compliance testing and tests of detail), each of which should be supported by working papers. The structure and format of these papers can be based on internal control questionnaires (ICQs), an example of which is given in Fig. 3.2.

Systems evaluation

This phase concerns the planning and overall framework of a project, in terms of the critical parameters of cost and quality. A subsidiary set of parameters may be devised to relate to a particular stage of the project which is being audited. For example, during construction, the subject of an internal control questionnaire might be variations and site instructions. Table 3.3 identifies a number of typical systems which could be evaluated at different stages during a construction project.

Once the parameters which are critical to the success of a project have been identified, the steps represented in Fig. 3.1 may be considered. The record of a system should describe the system as it is actually used rather than the form in which it was originally intended to be used. Once the system has been recorded, and before evaluation proceeds, a 'walk through test' may be carried out (i.e. take every step in the procedure and work through it) to check

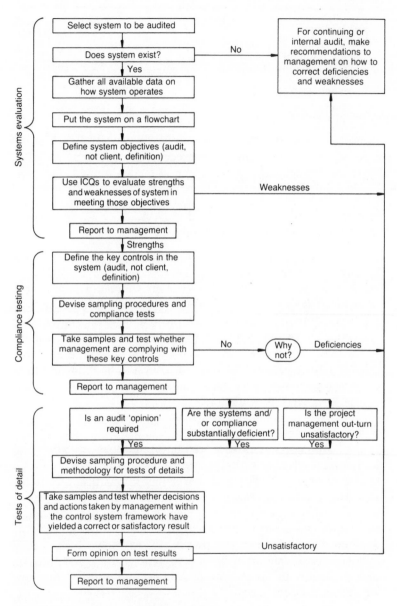

Fig. 3.1. Contract audit flowchart

Topic: Appointment of consultants
Control objective: (1) To ensure that the roles of consultants are clearly defined
　　　　　　　　(2) etc.

System checklist	Yes	No	Working paper ref.
1. (Primary question) Are the roles of consultants fully defined in writing by the client before consultants' proposals are invited?			
2. (Secondary question) Are the consultants' roles checked for scope and completeness by a suitably qualified member of the client's staff before consultants' proposals are invited?			

Fig. 3.2.   Example of an ICQ

that the record is complete and correct. A typical evaluation procedure consists of the following.

- Definition (by the auditor, independently of the client) of the control objectives of the system.
- Preparation of an internal control questionnaire in which the auditor devises a series of questions to assess the strengths and weaknesses of a system and to test whether an objective of control is capable of being met by the system. These questions should be designed so that a positive answer indicates a strength, a negative answer a weakness. The implications of a weakness should be recorded in a working paper together with any recommendations.

Compliance testing

The purpose of compliance testing is to discover whether, and if so, how, a system is actually used. It is one thing to have a good system in place and then to discover that in practice, on site for example, a different system is used or that there is no system in use. The compliance phase may involve carrying out interviews, examining the client's accounting records or an engineer's or quantity surveyor's working papers, for example. Testing may involve an examination of individual items as they pass through each procedure in the system or the selection of different items for each procedure tested.

An example of compliance testing might be a review of a system for the procurement of free issue equipment. The system might stipulate that

- the tender brief be fully defined before bids are invited
- no amendments are made to the brief after bids have been invited
- all equipment contracts are let competitively
- all equipment should be delivered on site to the main contractors on a specified date
- the supplier should commission the equipment and prepare operations and maintenance manuals
- a warranty for the equipment should run from the date of hand-over of the main contract works
- stage payments should be made when the equipment is delivered on site, at full commissioning and at hand-over of the main contract works.

Each of these stages would be examined against records of the client, equipment supplier and main contractor. Documentary checks might be supplemented with results of site inspections to discover whether equipment was stored solely on site, whether it had been incorporated into the works, whether stage payments had been made on time and for the agreed amount. One particular consideration to note would be the date on which a warranty began to take effect, especially if the main contract works were delayed.

Tests of details

Although tests of details are not always necessary, they are needed for an external audit, when evidence of financial values is required and when weaknesses have been exposed during systems evaluation and compliance testing. The sample selected should be properly established and of an appropriate size based on whether a misstatement of a particular size or frequency would affect the interpretation of data and any points of weakness identified during systems evaluation and compliance testing.

The purpose of these tests is to look for overstatement or understatement and to examine the quality of management decisions which fall outside the scope of the systems in place for a contract. The latter purpose would not feature in an audit of a public sector project. Examination of the quality of management decisions is included to ensure that lessons are learnt for the future

Table 3.3. Systems to be examined

Stage	System to be examined
Project appraisal	1. Application of relevant criteria in assessing the need for the project.
	2. Consideration and evaluation of alternative solutions.
	3. Financial appraisal techniques used are appropriate to the project, are correctly applied and used consistently in evaluating the alternatives.
Design	1. Suitability of the team preparing the design brief. This will include its composition, terms of reference, overall expertise and reporting systems.
	2. Engagement of a technically competent, well co-ordinated design team.
	3. Well-planned and strictly controlled timetable.
	4. Regular reviews of costs.
	5. Minimum number of design changes.
Tender	1. Selection of the tendering method.
	2. Selection of the form of contract.
	3. Selection of contractors invited to tender.
	4. Regulation of the tendering procedure.

and to provide data needed for the revision of systems if this proves to be necessary.

The size of the sample tested should be related to the strengths and weaknesses identified in the systems evaluation. If the systems are weak the sample size may need to be increased. The process of selection may be either judgmental (relying heavily on an individual auditor's skill and expertise) or statistical (as is often the case in external audits). Size might be determined by 'materiality' and assessment of risk. Materiality is the monetary amount of mis-statement which would affect the user of an account; the amount is a matter of judgement depending on the circumstances of the case. Assessment of risk involves consideration

Stage	System to be examined
	5. Criteria for tender evaluation.
	6. Letting of the contract.
Construction	1. Provision of financial information and reporting procedures which enable costs to be adequately controlled.
	2. On-site control regulating valuations of work for interim payments.
	3. Examination and control of price fluctuations.
	4. Control and issue of variations.
	5. Receipt and evaluation of contractual claims.
	6. Quality control which involves continuous monitoring of the works.
	7. Timeliness and accuracy of management information.
Post-completion	1. Completeness and accuracy of final account.
	2. Recovery of liquidated damages where appropriate.
	3. Post-completion assessment of cost and time variances, i.e. the differences between the original estimates and the actual outcomes.

of the impact and importance of risk on the overall scheme. Where systems have been shown to be weak, the risk would be high.

Conclusion

It should be apparent from the brief description given that a contract audit is capable of providing a means for improving the management and control of a contract. In this respect it could feature as an aspect of the internal audit of a company. Alternatively, if used as part of the external audit process, a contract audit may demonstrate to one party that the contract is being managed efficiently and effectively.

4 Financing construction projects

This chapter provides a brief introduction to the financing of construction projects. It covers types and sources of finance and outlines the steps to be taken when seeking project finance. It also refers to some recent developments in funding public sector projects. The term 'project' is used to cover all construction activity, whether building a road, houses, a factory, refurbishing an office block or a new leisure attraction. Most of these projects have one thing in common. They cost a great amount of money and represent substantial investments to the organizations or people sponsoring them.

Why is finance required?

At the simplest level, a company may finance its new factory through its own cash resources. These may be insufficient and other sources of finance are required. The project's sponsor may also seek other sources of finance to limit his or her risk from the project. A project is at risk from failure for a number of reasons. Construction delays, cost over-runs, technological change, increased interest rates, market factors such as depressed product prices may all lead to cost over-runs or failure to achieve the projected return on the project. By seeking partners to develop a project, the sponsor can not only spread the risk of failure (and also the rewards of success) but also achieve the best balance of expertise and contribution.

Choice of method of financing

The most appropriate method of financing a project depends on

- the project's characteristics
- the sponsor's objectives.

46

Project characteristics

The types and sources of finance available will be governed by factors such as

- purpose of project
- cost of development
- revenue/operating costs
- time to complete and for return
- complexity of construction and design
- risks
- ownership and management
- availability of grants or financial support
- tax position.

For example, financing suitable for a pre-let office development will not be appropriate for a leisure complex. Such an office development generally offers good underlying security and guaranteed future income to the investor or lender. An urban regeneration scheme may possibly require some form of grant or other incentive financing to be viable, when capital and operating costs are taken into account.

Sponsor's objectives

The selection of a method of financing must reflect the sponsor's objectives for the project. These objectives will almost certainly be conflicting. The method of financing should ensure the optimum solution.

The huge diversity of construction projects and the range of organizations and businesses involved mean that financing is a complex subject. New methods are constantly evolving to meet the needs of businesses, developers, investors, construction companies, government organizations and other project sponsors. It is only possible to highlight the basic points and common principles in this chapter. In the remainder of this chapter the following areas are described

- types of finance
- sources of finance
- obtaining project finance.

47

Types of finance

The types of finance are almost infinite. Here the categories of equity, debt, and other types of financing are used. Several different types of finance may be used together to fund one project.

Equity

A project may be financed by equity finance in a company specifically set up to undertake the project, or by new equity introduced into an existing company. In the case of equity finance, an investor provides a company with cash in exchange for shares in the company. The investor normally has the right to vote on matters concerning the company.

In return for the investment, the investor will receive a share in the company's profits (after tax and interest), which is called a dividend. The investor will also benefit from any capital growth of the company's assets. For the investor to benefit from any increase in the value of a company it is essential for a market to exist for the shares. Shares in public companies are traded in the Stock Exchange. Other avenues include private placings (or sale) of shares with institutions and private investors and the Unlisted Securities Market.

Debt

Debt financing occurs where a sum of money (the principal) is borrowed for a period of time and the borrower makes interest payments and principal repayments according to an agreed timetable. Although debt financing comes in many different forms, there are two main categories: debentures and loans.

Debentures

A debenture is a document issued by a company in exchange for money lent to the company. The company agrees to pay the lender a stated rate of interest and also to repay (or to redeem) the principal at some future date. Debentures can be traded in the same way as shares. The interest paid to debenture holders is deductible when calculating taxable profits, unlike dividend payments.

Debentures may be discounted, that is, offered for sale by a company at a price which is below the redemption value of the debenture. This is done to make the debenture more attractive to the investor. The tax treatment of discounted debentures is very complex but in many cases the 'discount' may be treated as a deduction when computing the profits of a company which reduces the cost of the discount to a company.

Loan finance

Many construction projects will involve some element of loan finance. The precise terms and conditions of a loan will depend on the criteria of the lender and the borrower and the type of project. The main features which will need to be agreed are

- repayment method
- interest rates
- security
- duration
- fees
- trigger clauses.

Some of the key features of each of these will now be described.

Repayment methods. There are several options for structuring repayment of interest and principal.

- *Mortgage.* Repayments are calculated so that the total amount paid at each instalment is constant, but the capital and interest proportions vary. Initially this means that the proportion of capital repayment is very small, but the proportion progressively increases throughout the period covered by the mortgage.

- *Equal instalments of principal.* The amount of principal repaid is constant with each payment. The total amount paid decreases over time, as it consists of a constant principal repayment plus interest on the outstanding principal.

- *Maturity.* The principal is repaid at the end of the loan period in one sum. This payment structure is particularly suited to projects which generate a large capital sum on completion.

Other variations on possible repayment structures include a moratorium on capital repayments (and possibly also interest payments) for a period at the beginning of the loan. This structure is useful where a project does not begin to generate revenue until completed. The value of the principal repayment may be increased

49

during the period of the loan, perhaps to coincide with rent reviews.

Interest. The interest charged on a loan will be governed by money market rates (which vary daily). The lender will also charge a premium for the risks, perceived by the lender, surrounding the project and the borrower. Interest rates may be fixed for the period of the loan or, as is often the case, expressed as a percentage of the standard base rate (such as the London inter-bank overnight rate). Quite sophisticated interest rate arrangements can be organized. For example, a borrower may negotiate a floating rate loan where an upper and/or lower limit is set on the interest rate. It is sometimes possible for a swap to be arranged, so that a company that wants a fixed rate loan, but finds it cheaper to arrange a floating rate loan, can swap its floating rate loan for one with a fixed rate arranged by a company that prefers a floating rate loan.

Security

Conventionally lenders seek to limit their risk of the borrower defaulting by insisting that the borrower provides good security to support the loan. This usually takes the form of a charge on the assets of a company or a guarantee from a credit-worthy organization or institution.

Non-recourse lending

The sums involved with a major capital project may be too large for the participants to provide a guarantee. A relatively recent development which seeks to overcome this problem is non-recourse lending.

Non-recourse lending is the term used for a loan where the project itself rather than the company's assets as a whole is the security offered to the lender. The lender accepts that the surplus cashflow over operating costs will cover the cost of interest payments arising from a debt, or that the building or project itself has a realizable capital value.

The advantage of non-recourse lending from the point of view of a developer or promoter is that it becomes possible to structure the deal so that the entire transaction does not appear in the annual report and accounts. In practice, banks will seek to minimize their exposure to risk by building in several safeguards such as requiring the developer to give certain guarantees: for example on completion and cost over-runs. This turns a pure non-recourse loan into a limited recourse loan.

Fees. Depending on the status of the borrower, fees may be charged by the lender for arranging the loan, managing the loan throughout the period of the loan, early payment and failure to take up the loan.

Trigger clauses. Trigger clauses define the conditions when the balance of the amount outstanding becomes due. They are often written into loan agreements with banks. Examples include non-payment of a loan instrument, change in ownership of the project and exceeding a set level of total company debt.

Other types of finance

There are three other types of finance which can be relevant to construction projects

- leasing
- countertrade
- grants and incentives.

Leasing

Leasing is a method of medium- or short-term finance used to fund an asset. The main characteristic of a leasing agreement is that the owner of the asset (the lessor) allows a third party (the lessee) the use of the asset in exchange for regular lease payments.

The two basic types of lease are the finance lease and the operating lease. A finance lease lasts for a substantial portion of the life of an asset. The risks and rewards of ownership effectively pass to the lessee. An operating lease lasts for a much shorter period of time than the economic life of the asset and the lessor retains the risks and rewards of ownership.

When capital allowances were available for expenditure on plant and equipment and industrial buildings, the cost of a lease was often less than the cost of financing debt to acquire the asset, because the lessor was able to utilize the tax benefits more effectively than the lessee. Changes in tax law which resulted in the phasing out of capital allowances have removed some of the tax advantages of leasing.

Countertrade

At its simplest, countertrade is the exchange of goods for goods, rather than for cash. It has become an important feature of business with developing countries and eastern European countries which do not have the financial or borrowing capability to make large investments in plant, machinery or construction projects.

Countertrade may take forms such as counterpurchase, which requires suppliers to a country to buy a certain amount of goods in return, or barter, where goods are exchanged for other goods. For example, oil is used as payment by oil producing countries for goods and services.

There are significant problems and risks associated with countertrade. It can be costly and inefficient because of commission for brokers to assist in disposing of the goods, delays in finding a buyer and insurance to cover the risk of non-delivery. It can be extremely complicated to set-up. It can also be extremely risky, particularly where the deal involves commodities which have rapidly fluctuating prices such as oil.

Grants and incentives

A number of grants and incentives are available for projects which are socially desirable, but not commercially viable without support. Grant help in the UK is concentrated on schemes providing employment, housing and other facilities in specific areas designated by the government as eligible for assistance. The government may change the grants available, so it is essential to obtain up-to-date information.

Grants. The characteristics of the main grants available are summarized in Table 4.1 which includes grants made available by the European Community, for which some areas in the UK, characterized by industrial decline, may be eligible to apply. The two main grants are from the European Regional Development Fund and European Social Fund. The latter is specifically for revenue expenditure for activities such as training; the emphasis is on job creation. The following comments should be borne in mind when considering making an application for a grant.

- It will be a time-consuming process.
- Some grants are paid directly to the developer; others are paid to the local authority or other public body. In the latter case it will be necessary to work closely with the local authority in carrying out a capital project.

Table 4.1. Summary of main grants available in the UK for capital expenditure

Grant	Awarding body	Eligible schemes	Who can apply	Level of award
European Regional Development Fund	European Community	Schemes for industry, craft industries and services, infrastructure investment and the promotion of tourism. Emphasis on job creation. Restricted to specific areas in the UK.	Public sector. Private sector grant in the UK is used to increase regional selective assistance.	Up to 50% of public sector capital expenditure.
Derelict Land Grant	Department of the Environment	Reclamation of derelict land.	Local authorities.	100% for local authorities.
Regional Selective Assistance	Department of Trade and Industry	Most manufacturing and certain service activities.	Private sector.	Minimum required for the project to go ahead.
City Grant	Department of the Environment	Capital investment in designated priority areas, project value over £200 000. Grant required because costs (plus reasonable profits) exceed value. Projects provide jobs, private housing and other benefits.	Private sector.	Minimum required for project to go ahead. Target gearing of 1:4 grant and other public sector funding to private sector funding.

- As it is usually necessary to demonstrate that the project will not go ahead without the grant, work cannot start until the grant application has been accepted.
- One of the objectives of grant finance is to act as an incentive for investment from the private sector. Typically, a ratio of 1:4 public:private finance is required.
- Before making a grant application, up-to-date information on the latest regulations, eligibility and procedures should be obtained.

Enterprise zones. Twenty five enterprise zones have been designated up to May 1990 throughout the UK. They range in size from 50 to 450 hectares. The benefits to industrial and commercial firms in enterprise zones are available for 10 years from the date of designation. The main benefits are as follows.

- 100% allowances for capital expenditure on buildings. Capital expenditure on plant and machinery will not normally qualify unless it is of a type which can be commonly found fixed to the building such as an air-conditioning system or a lift. It should be noted that such allowances are not available on the land element of any commercial building.
- Exemption from business rates on industrial and commercial buildings.
- A liberal planning regime with automatic consent for most types of capital project.

Taxation. Almost all grants received are regarded for tax purposes as reducing expenses incurred, or reducing the cost of the development in question for the purposes of calculating capital allowances. The significant exception to this is a regional development grant (RDG). Where an RDG is received, capital allowances can generally still be claimed on the full cost of the asset in question.

Sources of finance

The nature of the project and the type of finance required will determine the most appropriate source of finance. The criteria for assessing the likely return on a project and attitudes for the risks involved will differ between sources of finance.

Banks

The clearing banks are important sources of short to medium-term finance. Lending policies vary widely between different banks as well as between individual branches. Most leading merchant banks have established their own property investment departments and have been at the forefront of developing innovative methods of financing projects through equity and long-term debt. A number of foreign banks have developed considerable expertise in the area of project finance. On overseas developments, a foreign bank may well be able to offer specialist assistance with matters such as currency and tax advice.

Building societies

The Building Societies Act 1986 removed some of the restrictions on lending by building societies. The Act allows building societies to enter into such schemes as equity share and deferred purchase. Building societies are an important source of funds to residential developers. Methods of funding such developments include an agreed allocation of mortgage funds to a particular scheme, or the ' financing of a proportion of land and development costs on the understanding that the developer will market that society's services to prospective purchasers.

Institutions

The institutions, i.e. pension funds, insurance funds and trust funds, generally require a fixed, steady income stream and a low level of risk when making an investment or lending money. They will generally consider construction developments only on prime sites with few planning problems, preferably a freehold pre-let scheme, using an established developer. They usually look for large schemes in which to invest. However, the institutions are becoming more flexible and may consider short-term finance. They have also become more prepared to undertake their own developments.

Construction companies

Major construction companies are often prepared to invest their own funds in a project, or to arrange a loan on their own behalf in return for construction work. This will be referred to in more detail in connection with recent developments in financing construction projects.

Property investment and development companies

The large property investment and development companies may be prepared to finance a project by direct loan or guarantee, usually in return for an equity share in the project.

Sources of finance for overseas projects

A number of additional sources of finance are open to overseas projects, in particular

- national or international development banks
- export credit finance.

National or international development banks

National development organizations and regional or international agencies sometimes offer long-term loans for certain classes of projects at low rates of interest. Each organization or agency has its own lending criteria and the eligibility of a specific project will depend on its size, purpose and sponsors.

Development banks tend to take a long time to evaluate a project and are likely to impose conditions such as putting out all construction and equipment contracts to competitive tender. However, they can be helpful in attracting other sources of finance once the project has been approved and will finance supporting infrastructure.

Examples of development agencies are the European Development Bank, the World Bank, the Opec Fund, the African Development Bank and the Inter-American Development Bank.

Export credit finance

Export credit finance should be considered where a project requires capital goods and associated services to be imported because

- the term of the loan can sometimes be longer than the term for commercial funds
- the rate of interest is often subsidized and fixed for the life of the loan
- the loan is very often available in both local and foreign currency
- the buyer credit itself will provide for a loan of up to 85% of the cost of eligible goods and services.

Export credit agencies provide insurance against certain defaults to the exporter and guarantees to specified banks against which the banks advance the appropriate currency at a preferential interest rate. The buyer is then guaranteed the availability of finance which is fixed for the life of the loan. In effect, importers of capital equipment under an export credit system are provided, as buyers, with fixed-term funds at subsidized interest rates.

Obtaining project finance

A number of basic steps are essential in obtaining project finance, irrespective of the nature and size of a project. What differs between projects is the complexity and scope of work required at each step. A well planned approach to obtaining finance, supported by the appropriate documentation, is not only more likely to achieve the required finance, it also puts the sponsor in a stronger position when negotiating with the potential source of finance.

The steps involved are set out in Fig. 4.1. In practice some of the steps will be carried out in parallel and the process may be iterative, with new information necessitating the review of previous analysis and decisions. Each of the steps is briefly discussed here. As will be seen, a great deal of preparation is required before the first discussion with a potential source.

Fig. 4.1. Obtaining project finance

Step 1: define project sponsor's objectives

A clear statement of the project sponsor's objectives is an essential first step in the process. This establishes the criteria against which the methods of finance can be assessed. Different objectives and competing priorities of the sponsors have to be balanced, especially in the case of joint ventures.

Step 2: project appraisal

The feasibility of the project should be appraised rigorously before any financial commitments are made. Most governments, international agencies, investors and lenders will require a detailed feasibility study before deciding to participate. Chapter 5 deals with this subject in more detail.

Step 3: establish the preferred method of financing

The preferred method of financing is established by considering the characteristics of the project, the sponsor's objectives and the impact that each of the financing options will have on the financial return from the project. It is often helpful to approach a potential source of finance at this stage for informal discussions on the terms and conditions of finance likely to be available for the project.

Step 4: develop the appropriate financial structure

There are a number of options when setting up the financial structures for a project

- a trust
- a subsidiary of an existing company
- a nominee or jointly owned company
- limited or general partnerships
- joint ventures.

The selection of the most appropriate structure will depend on the degree to which participants are prepared to commit themselves financially, their desire to retain ownership and the risks and obligations entailed. Potential lenders will seek to influence the financial structure of the project to minimize their risk or to maximize their return.

Factors which must be taken into account when evaluating potential financial structures include tax and legal considerations and the credit-worthiness of participants. The management of the project and procedures to resolve disputes are also important considerations. Legal and tax changes affecting the project's finances will need to be monitored continuously and their impact assessed and minimized where possible.

Step 5: discussions with potential sources

The form of these discussions will depend on the scale and complexity of the project, as well as the sophistication of the financing package. For a relatively straightforward project, the sponsors may have identified two or three banks as potential sources. The banks will require certain information on the project before discussions go beyond a general commitment of interest. The information usually required is listed in Table 4.2. The detail needed will depend on the specific requirements of the bank, but they will wish to be satisfied that

- all risks attached to the project have been identified
- the project cash flow will cover the cost of repayment of loan capital and interest
- adequate security is available.

For most large projects it is usual to prepare a more formal document, called a financial memorandum, as a means of attracting potential sources of finance. The content of this document will be similar to the information listed in Table 4.2.

Lenders apply a number of standard techniques to the assessment of a project

- where an established company is the borrower, the lender will study the published accounts
- an analysis is made of key financial ratios (for example, current assets to current liabilities)
- a careful examination is made of the security offered
- a sensitivity analysis is performed to test the effect, on the project's viability, of changes in important factors, such as interest rates, construction costs and revenue.

Step 6: evaluate offers

The sponsor of the project must evaluate offers and calculate the total cost of using a selected finance package and compare it with the costs of other sources of finance. The offer should meet

59

Table 4.2. Information usually required by sources of finance

---

Background, history and organization of the project.
Project costs, itemizing

- land
- construction
- fees and other management expenditure
- fixtures, furniture and equipment
- financing costs.

Project programme.
Ownership structure and funding vehicle.

Full financial appraisal

- operating costs
- revenue.

Review of raw materials supplies.
Licences, grants, remits, leases required/obtained.
Economic and market outlook for industry of project.
Ownership structure, identity of sponsors/shareholders.
Operations and management arrangements.
Financial package required.
Security.

---

the sponsor's objectives. Where it does not, the sponsor must understand the effect of this and consider whether it is acceptable or not.

It will be necessary at this stage to rework the financial projections of the project using the financing terms offered to understand fully the impact of each proposition.

Step 7: negotiate and finalize financing agreement
This stage will involve an iterative process of assessing the financial and legal consequences of proposed changes to the details of the financing agreement.

Step 8: management of finance
Management of project finance should continue throughout the life of a project. The receipt of cash into the project, whether in the form of equity or loan, will not match the project cash flows. Cash flows should be managed to optimize the return from cash

received and to minimize the cost of finance. The investment of surplus cash can be a complex process, as the funds must be available to meet commitments as they fall due.

Recent developments

In addition to the conventional sources and methods of financing construction projects which have been described here, recent developments point to a more flexible approach to the way in which public sector infrastructure projects are financed. Following the withdrawal in 1989 of the Treasury's controls on private sector infrastructure financing, new methods of construction finance may become more important, in particular the build-operate-transfer (BOT) method.

Under this method the contractor is the promoter of the project. No two BOT schemes are likely to be the same but a special purpose company is usually formed to enter into the principal contracts and loan agreements. The BOT method draws together contractors and financiers to design, finance, build and operate a utility for an agreed concessionary period which generates revenue for its promoters by tolls or supply charges. The Channel Tunnel project is a good example of this method. Ten British and French companies combined to form the Channel Tunnel Group (subsequently Eurotunnel and TML) which took a 50 year lease on the Channel Tunnel. The East London River Crossing is another example. Trafalgar House plc is constructing a bridge across the River Thames above the Dartford Tunnels, which it runs, using the tolls to pay for the bridge. Debts on both the bridge and tunnels at Dartford are expected to be wiped out within 17 years when the structure will be transferred to the government, and the contractors will have recovered the costs and made a profit.

In addition to the familiar contracting problems, a contractor involved in a BOT scheme will carry the promoter's responsibilities for securing the project finance, minimizing and spreading risk, legal and insurance issues. The contractor will also need to set up an operating body to run the utility during its concessionary period. Financing the project is likely to be the most difficult operation. The biggest risk occurs during construction, before revenue is generated. Quoted shares may overcome this problem. Eurotunnel has demonstrated that shares may bring long-term project appeal to short-term investors. Where there is limited or no recourse to government to guarantee a scheme, the risks of the project after completion of construction may be offset by an agreement to index-link tolls or charges and by insurance guarantees.

A number of Third World and developing countries have developed BOT schemes in which UK contractors have been involved. Major civil engineering contractors have undoubtedly identified the potential business opportunities of these schemes. Not all projects will be suitable for BOT treatment, which depends on satisfying the private sector that the project is economically viable with available technologies and practices. The method of finance is relatively novel and as yet untried by most contractors but, as is the case when trying to start up any project, potential pitfalls and problems can be circumvented by using consultants, particularly in the early stages to provide off-take forecasts, preliminary designs, financial and legal advice, and subsequently for project management.

5 Project appraisal

The purpose of project appraisal is to evaluate a proposed capital investment which is irreversible and involves risk. Detailed appraisal methods are needed, taking account of factors such as size, type, location and timing as well as taxation and method of financing. An appraisal should answer two key questions

- what return will be achieved if the assumptions are correct?
- what is the likelihood of these assumptions being correct?

Appraisals should also compare different projects which compete against each other for scarce resources such as funds, people, land or raw materials and allow the correct decision to be made. This chapter places project appraisal in context, discusses methods of appraisal and describes best practice.

Project cycle

The project cycle, shown in Fig. 5.1, may be recognized in almost all projects. It is useful to note how project appraisal integrates with the rest of the project and its dependence on effective management of the project if the assumptions are to hold good. Notice also the inclusion of a post project review. This ensures that the relevant lessons are distilled and fed back into the appraisal stage of subsequent projects.

Definition of objectives

An explicit statement of the objectives of each project is vital, particularly if there is a joint venture where different parties may have different objectives. For example, in urban regeneration the local authority's objective may be job creation, the objective of central government may be the reduction of crime, the contractor's

63

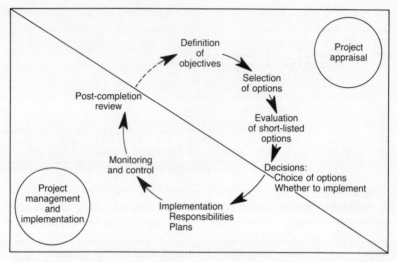

Fig. 5.1. Project cycle

objective may be profit from construction, the developer's objective may be profit from selling on a let facility, and the operator's objective may be operating profits. These differing objectives can be balanced, but only if they are resolved at the outset, before money is committed or spent. It is also necessary to decide on the balance between cost, time and quality objectives, and how this will be resolved if problems arise during the design and construction phases. This may all sound very obvious, but experience of major projects which have gone wrong shows that the principal cause is often unclear or conflicting objectives rather than poor project appraisal.

Selection of options

This is the stage for creative thinking and imaginative ideas — how to convert vision into reality. For example, there are numerous ways of making a new river crossing: bridge or tunnel, steel or concrete, various types of construction and financing options. Each option which appears to be attractive must be considered and designed at least in outline to see if it meets the objectives for the project. These must then be short-listed; the detailed appraisal can only be done in practice on a limited number of options.

To ensure that the short-list produces a robust selection, it is necessary to appraise each of the options against common criteria. It is vital that all external constraints are known at this stage, otherwise all the short-listed options may be for bridges when, for environmental reasons or because of the proximity of an airport, only a tunnel is possible.

Evaluation of short-listed options

This is the core of the appraisal. However, it will not be successful unless the objectives have been stated clearly and all the practical options considered.

Decisions

Realistic evaluation of the options allows a clear decision on whether to proceed or not. The decision point is particularly important for joint venture projects. New information may have been uncovered by the appraisal which alters the objectives or the ability of the parties to continue to participate. Once a project which meets the predetermined criteria has been found the natural inclination is to proceed as quickly as possible, but ignoring changed circumstances will cause problems.

Project appraisal

A project appraisal, for example of an urban regeneration project to redevelop a town centre site, would include an analysis of the total operating environment and evaluation of appropriate solutions to reveal maximum market potential. It will provide an integration of

- economic appraisal
- market analysis
- design/cost evaluation
- contract strategy
- operating strategy
- financial appraisal
- development funding
- tax effects
- overall commercial appraisal.

The economic appraisal will include reviewing local demographic and regional consumption and expenditure patterns, discussions with local authority officials to identify local development plans and discussions with bodies such as tourist boards to identify what developments are taking place elsewhere.

The market analysis will need to identify current competitors, in terms of their volume and price patterns, catchment areas for different facilities, future changes in the supply and demand balance, the likely range of revenues for each facility in the development and the best combination of facilities, which maximizes the opportunities for synergy.

The design and cost evaluation will be based on a facilities brief derived from the market analysis appropriate for the site, a contract strategy and overall programme with defined roles for the technical professionals, a view of how easy the project would be to build and life cycle costs and elemental costing. With this brief the impact of changes (for example, smaller or larger units, different combinations, phased programmes) may be understood easily. The contract strategy will be based on the trade-off between time, cost and quality, attitude to risk and availability of project management. The review of operating strategy will highlight operating skills required for success, sources of labour, fixed and variable cost characteristics, opportunities for improving viability by increasing revenues or reducing costs, programming of the total scheme and property strategy. The review will answer the question: is the best use of property being made both in the short and long term?

After these stages have been completed, the financial appraisal can be carried out. Detailed appraisal techniques are used to examine the overall financial viability of the project against predetermined investment criteria (such as a post-tax discounted cash-flow return of 15%, explained in the following section) and objectives previously set; and to test the sensitivity of the project against changes in key variables (such as revenue, capital cost, interest rates, and time period).

The appraisal should take account of different methods of funding the project including the availability of grants and incentives (discussed in chapter 4) and the effects of taxation on which the advice of competent tax experts should be sought. In relation to the latter, consideration will need to be given to the possible incidence of income or corporation tax, taking into account taxable profits arising from project cash flows. Account should also be taken of relief which may be available for capital expenditure on assets. The purchaser of a completed development, for example a factory, who intends to use the development for his or her own trade purposes or lease it to a person using it for trade purposes may be able to claim capital allowances.

Capital allowances which may be available are as follows.

- *Industrial buldings allowances.* These are claimed by the purchaser of an industrial building who is using it for his or her own trade or leasing it to another for that person's trade, at the rate of 4% per annum on cost. Other rates may apply where the development is acquired second hand, or is merely a refurbishment of an existing industrial building. Retail developments will not qualify for industrial buildings allowances.

- *Capital allowances on plant and machinery.* Any part of the cost of a development which is attributable to plant and machinery will generally qualify for a 25% annual allowance if it is used for the purchaser's trade or leased by the purchaser to another for the purpose of the other's trade. All qualifying expenditure is usually pooled together, disposal proceeds deducted, and the 25% allowance is given on the net balance. The plant and machinery content of a development is an important planning area for tax purposes and detailed costings of the development assist in identifying any qualifying element.

- *Enterprise zones.* As already explained in chapter 4 a 100% allowance is available on the purchase of a commercial building in a designated enterprise zone.

- *Scientific research allowances.* A 100% capital allowance is available for capital expenditure on scientific research (for example, for the purchase of a laboratory). The Inland Revenue tends to regard pure research as qualifying and excludes research which is linked directly to commercial products.

Although the information given here was correct at the time of preparing this guide it is essential to obtain up to date information to take account of any changes in official policy.

For all of these types of capital allowance, where, on sale, the disposal proceeds exceed the cost of the asset less the allowances claimed, the disposal will give rise to a clawback of allowances equal to the smaller of the excess and the allowances claimed. Where the proceeds do not exceed the cost of the asset less the allowance claimed, an allowance equal to the shortfall will be given unless the original expenditure was pooled, in which case the balance of the pooled expenditure after deducting the disposal proceeds will continue to be written down at 25% per annum.

In addition consideration will need to be given in the course of project appraisal to the impact of VAT on supplies and services to which reference has already been made briefly in chapter 2.

A number of important changes to UK VAT law have recently been made. These came into effect on (or in some cases after) 1 April 1989. Many supplies in the construction and property sector are now subject to 15% VAT which can have a significant impact if the ultimate user of a building is, say, partially exempt and is therefore largely unable to recover VAT costs, for example, a bank or an insurance company.

The final element of the project appraisal process involves an overall commercial appraisal of the project. The results of an integration of the above factors should be analysed with reference to the objectives of the organization concerned and the expected risks and rewards of the project. Project appraisal involves many calculations which must be carried out a number of times to produce a proper senstivitiy analysis. It may be helpful to use a microcomputer for this purpose. Although there are a number of project appraisal software programs available it is frequently quicker to construct a simple model using a spreadsheet program.

Project appraisal for public sector projects follows a similar discipline. Some government departments (such as the Department of Health) publish guidance notes on option appraisal. The

Table 5.1. Cash flow in project A over four years: £ million

Year	Cash outflow	Cash inflow	Cumulative cash flow
0	(1·0)		(1·0)
1		0·3	(0·7)
2		0·3	(0·4)
3		0·3	(0·1)
4		0·3	0·2

Treasury publishes technical guidance on investment appraisal. These notes are designed to ensure that project appraisal does not concentrate solely on costs but gives priority to the objectives of the service. For example, health authorities are required to demonstrate that the care of patients and the services they receive have been considered in any project appraisal.

It should also be noted that detailed arrangements describing the procedural framework for managing and processing capital building schemes are available for use in the health service.

Financial measurements

Cash flow is fundamental to the methods of financial appraisal described here. The following elements should be included in cash flows: cash in (such as debtors and other income); cash out (such as creditors and other expenditures); taxation in the period of payments; opportunity costs (such as the value of land already owned); and terminal value. Depreciation, interest and inflation should not be included in cash flows. On this basis the methods of investment appraisal described here may be used. Formerly 'payback' and the 'rate of return' were the two methods used most frequently, but discounting is more commonly used nowadays.

Payback

This is usually based on before-paying-tax figures. The criterion is the number of years before the pre-tax cash receipts from the project pay back the capital invested. For example, if a small, light rapid transit system (project A) costs £1 000 000 and its cash inflows are £300 000 per annum, the project will be paid back in year 4, as shown in Table 5.1.

Payback is a very simple and useful method, and hence it is popular. The main drawback, however, is its failure to reflect the relative financial attractiveness of projects, as it is biased in favour of the short term. This can have a marked effect on an investment decision. For example, consider an alternative transit system (project B) which costs £1 000 000 and has cash inflows of £300 000 per year for four years and £500 000 per year for the next six years. Project A has cash inflows of £300 000 per year for ten years. The cash flows of the two projects are compared in Table 5.2. The Table highlights the drawback of the payback method. Although both projects have the same payback period (3.3 years), project B is

69

more attractive in terms of net cash flow if the longer term is taken into account.

Rate of return

The rate of return is the profit (net of accounting depreciation) expressed as a percentage of the capital invested. This may be expressed either as a single year figure or as some form of average over the life of the project. Capital may be either the initial capital outlay including working capital or the average capital employed over the life of the project. For example, if the capital investment is £10 million and the annual profit for years 1−10 is £1 million, the average return on investment is 10% per annum.

This method is also deceptive because it takes no account of the timing of receipts. Profit in year two is regarded in exactly the same way as profit in year 10. If this method is based on initial capital costs, it strongly favours long-term projects (say, over ten years) against short-term ones and those with good cash receipts in the early years. If it is based on average capital costs, it favours short-term projects and those with large initial cash receipts against long-term projects.

Table 5.2. Comparison of cash flows in projects A and B over ten years: £ million

Year	Project A			Project B		
	Cash outflow	Cash inflow	Cumulative cash flow	Cash outflow	Cash inflow	Cumulative cash flow
0	(1·0)		(1·0)	(1·0)		(1·0)
1		0·3	(0·7)		0·3	(0·7)
2		0·3	(0·4)		0·3	(0·4)
3		0·3	(0·1)		0·3	(0·1)
4		0·3	0·2		0·3	0·2
5		0·3	0·5		0·5	0·7
6		0·3	0·8		0·5	1·2
7		0·3	1·1		0·5	1·7
8		0·3	1·4		0·5	2·2
9		0·3	1·7		0·5	2·7
10		0·3	2·0		0·5	3·2

Discounting

It is now commonly agreed that a better way of appraising projects is to use a method of discounting such as discounted cash flow (DCF) or net present value (NPV) as rate of return takes no account of the timing of receipts. Discounting is based on the recognition that money received one year hence is worth less than money received today because of the income that could have been earned by investing the capital now. Put simply, £100 received today could be invested at 10% per annum and so be worth £110 next year compared with the £100 received then. Reversing this statement, the present value of £110 to be received in one year's time is £100. Similarly, the discounting factor for payments made in one year's time is 100/110 or 0·91. The discounting calculation is the reverse of the compound interest calculation.

Discounted cash flow. The DCF return (often called the internal rate of return (IRR)) is the rate of return which discounts the cash income of a project to a present value (i.e. at the start of project) equal to its capital cost. If a project costing £1000 produces an end of year cash receipt of £388 for three years net of tax, the DCF return is 8% because

$$\frac{£388}{1·08} + \frac{£388}{1·08^2} + \frac{£388}{1·08^3} = £359 + £333 + £308$$
$$= £1000$$

Net present value. In using DCFs, reference is often made to NPV. This is the present value of the project's net cash flows discounted at the cost of capital less the initial capital cost. Therefore if the discount rate in the previous example was 5%

$$\frac{£388}{1·05} + \frac{£388}{1·05^2} + \frac{£388}{1·05^3} - £1000$$
$$= £370 + £352 + £335 - £1000$$
$$= £57$$
$$= NPV$$

If the cost of capital is 8%, then

$$NPV = £359 + £333 + £308 - £1000 = 0$$

This example shows that the DCF return is the rate of discounting which makes the NPV zero. In other words

$$\text{NPV} = \frac{C_1}{[1+r]} + \ldots + \frac{C_n}{[1+r]^n} - I$$

where C is the annual cash flow, r is the discount rate (%/100), I is the initial investment, and n is the number of years considered.

For example, a 10% discount rate would yield the following discount factors

year 1 $= 1/1 \cdot 1 \quad = 0 \cdot 909091$
year 2 $= 1/1 \cdot 1^2 = 0 \cdot 826446$
year 3 $= 1/1 \cdot 1^3 = 0 \cdot 751315$

Much technical debate has taken place about the advantages of using DCF (IRR) and NPV. Merrett and Sykes, the pioneers in this field, concluded that, on operational grounds, the NPV is generally preferable. The NPV method has become an acceptable method for determining the financial feasibility of a project. Like the IRR method, this method also recognizes that £1 today is worth more than £1 in the future. The NPV method simply discounts at an agreed discount rate. The project which shows the greatest cash surplus is the one preferred.

Inter-project comparison

NPVs can be used to choose between two projects by comparing the cash surplus when discounted at an agreed rate. For example project A has an initial cash outflow of £1 million and a cash inflow of £300 000/year for 10 years. Project B has the same initial cash outflow but has cash inflows of £200 000/year in years 1−4, and cash inflows of £400 000/year in years 5−10. At a discount rate of 20%, which project should be accepted? A comparison of the cashflows for the two projects is given in Table 5.3. As project A has the greater NPV, it should be the preferred option.

Project selection

Once the appraisal has been evaluated the project should be selected and submitted for approval. It is vital at this stage that the selected project is presented in a clear, concise and logical format. It should be robust enough to stand up to the most rigorous testing from the appraisal panel. The reason for this is simple. If

Table 5.3. *Discounted cash flows for projects A and B: £*

Year	Project A			Project B		
	Cash flows	Discount factor 20%	DCF	Cash flows	Discount factor 20%	DCF
0	(1 000 000)	1·000	(1 000 000)	(1 000 000)	1·000	(1 000 000)
1	300 000	0·833	249 900	200 000	0·833	166 600
2	300 000	0·694	208 200	200 000	0·694	138 800
3	300 000	0·579	173 700	200 000	0·579	115 800
4	300 000	0·482	144 600	200 000	0·482	96 400
5	300 000	0·402	120 600	400 000	0·402	160 800
6	300 000	0·335	100 500	400 000	0·335	134 000
7	300 000	0·279	83 700	400 000	0·279	111 600
8	300 000	0·233	69 900	400 000	0·233	93 200
9	300 000	0·194	58 200	400 000	0·194	77 600
10	300 000	0·162	48 600	400 000	0·162	64 800
Net			+257 900			+159 600

the project appraisal is flawed, or if the project only marginally exceeds the minimum rate of return specified by the organization, it is better that it should fail at the approval stage than be implemented with the risk of subsequent failure.

When selecting the project for presentation to the approving authority, it is therefore important to bear in mind the following questions

- does the project fit with the company's strategy and objectives?
- does the project provide a detailed description of the project and background?
- are there calculations highlighting the rate of return compared with the company's rate of return?
- what are the project assumptions?
- what are the benefits?

Project approval

Approval of a project in the private sector is normally given by a panel within a company (for example) consisting of senior managers and directors. The composition of the panel usually reflects the level of required expenditure. For example, in all but small companies a project of a few thousand pounds would probably be approved by a senior manager, whereas a multi-million pound project will probably require board approval. Each panel member should ensure that he or she thoroughly tests the case presented for project approval. This will involve questioning assumptions, ensuring that the project is consistent with company strategy and testing the project evaluation in detail.

Project implementation controls

Once a project has been approved controls should be established to monitor its progress, quality and costs. This usually involves

- detailed programming of the project
- detailed preparation of the specification of the project
- setting a project budget which can be used to assess progress towards completion of the programme.

In addition, before implementing a project the company should set targets against which the project can be assessed. This should normally be performed by a person (or team) who is completely independent of the project. These targets will enable the company to determine whether the project is meeting the established criteria. They should also indicate potential problems which, if rectified at a sufficiently early stage, will avoid the need for unnecessary expenditure of time and money in seeking to correct the position.

Post-completion review

Depending on the circumstances of the case, a review at this stage would be too late to have any impact on a project. However, it is a helpful way of determining whether any lessons can be learned for future projects. This will help to strengthen the capital budgeting system and should produce more satisfactory projects. When reviewing the completed project the auditor will usually seek to establish that the project was

- consistent with the company's strategy
- completed on time, to a specified quality and within budget
- progressed in line with management controls.

6   Controlling project costs

There are a number of principles applicable to the control of costs which apply to all stages of a project. This chapter examines the application of these principles at the various stages in construction projects and the roles of the different parties involved.

Although some projects have been completed within budget when cost control systems have been weak or, in some cases, non-existent, such projects are exceptional. In the majority of cases, keeping a project within budget depends on an efficient and effective system of cost control. From the information generated by such a system, it is possible to discover weaknesses, to identify past trends and to make realistic forecasts of the consequences of future decisions. Without an adequate system of cost control it may well be impossible to instil, let alone to sustain, the right attitude towards completing a project within budget by all those concerned.

Forecasting and control of costs

Essential features of forecasting and cost control are as follows.

- Managers and the systems which they use must give advance warning when a decision extending or improving the plan for the remaining work is necessary.
- A wide range of possible alternative courses of action should be considered.
- Sufficiently accurate cost forecasts (including consequential costs such as disruption to the works of introducing the decision) should be made of all the possible options identified. These forecasts should consider the effects of each option on the revenue as well as on the capital costs of the completed project.

- The chosen option must be the one which best fits the forecast cost for the total project. Normally if minimum cost is sought, the lowest cost solution should be chosen. However, the choice will not always be the lowest cost solution because time and performance factors are usually relevant. At this stage the use of any remaining contingency allowance has to be considered.
- After the decision has been made, the forecast costs of the chosen option are included in the total cost forecast for the remaining work.

If any of these features are not present the cost objective for the project is unlikely to be met.

Completion within budget depends on a combination of

- understanding the project objectives and decision-making process
- the ability to prompt control decisions
- the ability to make cost forecasts
- an effective policy for settling and controlling contingencies.

Contingency sums

Forecasts of cost are never accurate. Fig. 6.1 shows how the accuracy of the forecast of the final cost of a project gradually improves as the design is developed from a concept at the beginning of the feasibility stage. On completion of the design, the accuracy of the forecast cost increases with receipt of tenders but there will

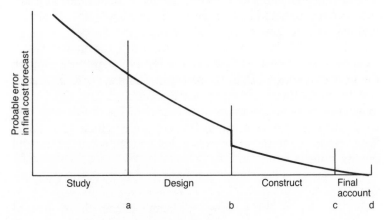

Fig. 6.1. Accuracy of cost forecasting

still be significant inaccuracy reflecting the likelihood of unforeseen events occurring, such as differing ground conditions and the introduction of variations. The precise cost of a project can only be determined when the final account (including any claims) is settled.

The possibility of overspending due to inevitable inaccuracy in the estimate should be guarded against by the inclusion of contingency sums. One of the ways in which the project manager may exert overall control of the project is by setting, allocating and subsequently controlling the release of appropriate contingency allowances.

The amount of the contingency sum should reflect the degree of uncertainty in the definition of the project and the firmness or otherwise of the budget. If it is imperative that the budget should not be exceeded, the contingency should be adequate to cover all possibilities. If the intention is to justify to the source of funds the need for additional finance as circumstances arise, the contingency sum can be lower.

If there are a number of different design specialists involved in a project, each specialist group must work within the budgets which have been set. The amount of contingency sum allocated to each of these budgets should reflect the degree of uncertainty within the work of the design team as well as the degree of control which the project manager wishes to retain over the team. Design teams should be allocated a total budget within which they agree to provide a design to the appropriate quality. A further contingency sum or reserve should be kept for the project manager to deal with matters outside the control of the design teams.

Each specialist design team must work within the budgets which have been set. Release of part of the reserve should be through the project manager. If all teams act in this way, overall control will be maintained. Keeping design teams on the right track depends largely on the terms of reference of the design brief and the goodwill of the teams. It is often desirable to include a budget limit within the terms of reference, taking into account time and quality criteria.

Control

As the size of the contingency sum reflects the degree of uncertainty, the amount of the sum required should decrease as the project proceeds. At regular intervals, usually monthly, the contingency previously agreed to be appropriate for that stage of the work should be added to the current estimate to produce the current forecast of the final cost. Any unspent and unrequired contingency sum identified by this process should be released to the client's reserve.

An appropriate calculation or formula for the amount of contingency required at any particular time should be agreed at the same time that the initial size of the contingency is determined. This method ensures that an appropriate amount of contingency sum is left at the end of the design and at the beginning of the construction stages and, more importantly, that pressure to limit costs applies to design teams in the early stages. This forces the teams to anticipate cost problems early enough for corrective action to be taken. The aim at all times should be to have the most accurate estimate of the final cost.

Cash constraints. Many clients, particularly government departments, have expenditure limits imposed on them. They will have a fixed budget to spend on construction, either in total or in particular financial years. The preparation by the client's project manager of a cash-flow forecast for the period of construction is often required. This may be requested to accompany each tender submitted. Analysis of contractor's cash flow projections and their discounting back to current prices may reveal that what appears to be the cheapest tender is not in fact so, or that it would exceed the client's budget at certain times. If the tender falls outside the client's cash profile requirement it would be sensible to ask the contractor to revise the programme or renegotiate change of payment terms. In any case cash-flow forecasts may be used by the client as a means of planning the client's own cash flow and controlling costs, and serve as a form of progress measurement.

Cost control during design

The cost of a project depends largely on decisions about the scope of the project which are taken during the briefing and design stages. Effective management of the design process is of major importance in controlling project costs. There are two main aspects to be borne in mind.

- All decisions taken during the design stage must be directed

79

towards achieving the quality, cost and time objectives of the client.

- The design process must be managed so that it is completed to quality within cost and time targets and with all necessary decisions having been taken and expressed fully and clearly in specifications and drawings.

The cost of design work may account for a significant proportion of the capital cost of a project. Design costs of 15% of the costs of construction are not unusual on multi-disciplinary projects. One method of controlling these costs is to link the production of drawings and obtaining planning permissions to payment. This can serve not only as a useful means of cost control but it also ensures that the client is not left until the end of the design stage without any information about the type of building which ultimately will be provided.

Control mechanisms

It is not possible to control cost in isolation because of the interdependence of quality, cost and time. It is therefore essential that the control mechanisms for each are put in place at the beginning of the design stage.

Quality. The brief should set the quality standards which the design has to meet. It should be a comprehensive document, approved by the client, which defines his or her requirements for the project. It should identify any matters requiring further development.

Costs. When the brief is being prepared, a cost plan should be developed on the basis of assumptions used in the project appraisal. This plan should be regularly updated as the design evolves so that at any moment in time it represents the best forecast of the final cost of the project. If the rate of expenditure is important to the client, the budget also needs to be expressed as a cash-flow forecast for the total project and as forecasts for financial years.

It is only by keeping an up to date total cost plan, which is revised to incorporate all new forecasts, that realistic comparisons with the budget cost can be made.

Time

The brief should establish the overall timetable of the project which should be agreed with the client and be compatible with the contract strategy. It should show all the stages of the project and the main outputs at each stage. The timetable should be reviewed and, if appropriate, should be modified as the project progresses.

Information for design control

Design management is an extensive subject but there are small points of technique about the information needed for control and the control of design information which are seldom discussed but deserve to be mentioned. For example, in a major project several design firms are normally involved. When dividing the total design effort into packages for each firm it is most important to define the boundaries of these packages clearly and comprehensively. The design process has been unnecessarily slow on many projects because the exchange of information between designers has been ineffective. When the design programme is set up, information can be exchanged efficiently by describing in detail the information to be exchanged.

The frequent circulation of a rapidly revised action list among members of the design team is not only a helpful source of information but a powerful stimulus towards making good progress. Experience has also shown that adherence to the design programme is more likely to be achieved if discussions and decisions at progress meetings are confined to refining plans for future action, drawing on lessons learnt from past experiences.

In all the exchanges of information during the design stage, frequent reference should be made to the objectives set for the project and the standards of the various components.

Cost control during construction

Cost control should not be limited to the conceptual or design phase alone. Within the parameters set when a contract is won there may be considerable scope for controlling costs during construction. Factors which affect the ability of a client or contractor to control costs during construction are described here.

Effect of types of contract

The ability of clients and the motivation of contractors to control costs during construction varies according to the type of contract used and the apportionment of risk and responsibility. The more risk the contractor is required to take, the more expensive the price is likely to be at the outset. If the client takes more of the risk, the contractor's tender price may be lower, but the client may have to pay extra sums as the contract proceeds and the risk becomes quantifiable in the light of claims and variations because of events such as unforeseen ground conditions. Ideally, risk and responsibility should be apportioned together because the party who is responsible for performing a task should carry the risk if it is carried out incorrectly. Risk is best allocated to the party who is best placed to minimize its effects.

Client's ability to control costs

The ability and effectiveness of a client in controlling costs during the construction phase depends primarily on how good the client is at minimizing changes and the effects of any unexpected events. This in turn depends on the amount and quality of work done by the client, or on his or her behalf, before and during construction.

Before construction

Quality of client brief and design. The more detailed and final the design is before tender, the fewer the changes to the design which may be needed after the contract has been awarded. The client or client's project manager must ensure that the brief to the design team is comprehensive and sufficient. This gives the design team a sound basis for their detailed design work. If the design phase is managed efficiently with no gaps in information or changes, the resultant design documents put out for tender will have minimized the need for variations to satisfy the original brief.

Effect of terms of contract. The choice of contract may also have a significant effect on the ability of the client to control costs. If there is a firm, fixed design which is let on a fixed price basis, the primary responsibility for control of construction costs is given to the contractor. If the design of the works is evolving as construction proceeds, and the contract is let on a cost reimbursable basis, responsibility for controlling costs lies principally with the client or with the client's representatives.

Onerous conditions of contract cost money. For example, if the client wishes to restrict the contractor to working in specified hours, or to restrict access to parts of the works, the client must expect to pay more.

Nominated subcontractors. The nomination of subcontractors, whereby the main contract or the engineer stipulates the name of a subcontractor whom the main contractor must employ, should generally be avoided unless, for example, it is necessary to retain specialist skills or to observe a time constraint.

The main contractor is not responsible for the selection of nominated subcontractors. Depending on the terms of the contract, delays by nominated subcontractors which affect the main contractor may result in claims against the client which can best be avoided if all of the subcontractors are selected by the main contractor.

Specification. Overspecification of materials or workmanship costs money. Specifications should be appropriate for the works resulting in the best value for money. The specification of untried or new technology, equipment or techniques has risks and the contractor has to make allowances for any exceptional remedial work which may be necessary.

During construction

Minimizing variations and new instructions. After a contract has been agreed any new instructions and variations to the works potentially cost money; if the client wishes to control costs it is essential that any such additions are controlled. If possible the client should restrict the introduction of changes in the scope of the works part way through the job except for safety reasons. The ability to do so will be determined by the form of the contract but alternatives such as letting 'change of scope' work as separate contracts, to be done after the main contract has finished, should be considered. In all cases variations must be priced, evaluated and approved before proceeding. In many cases this may not be practicable. In any case a record should be kept of events as they occur on site, the accuracy of which should be confirmed as soon as possible, to provide a basis on which any variations may be approved.

Responding promptly to unexpected events. If an unexpected event occurs, such as unforeseen ground conditions or the recognition of a deficiency in design information, steps must be taken immediately to respond to the event and to minimize its effects.

Although this may be the responsibility of the design or project management team, the employer should always be kept informed. After all, it is the employer's money which is being spent and the employer's view may be different from that of the employer's advisers.

Engineer's ability to control costs during construction

Larger contracts may include terms under which a person named as 'the Engineer', 'the Architect', or 'the Supervising Officer' has powers and duties to supervise and instruct a contractor. The terms of a contract may also enable that person to delegate some or all of his or her powers to representatives, typically a resident engineer on site. For convenience, the engineer is referred to here. Essentially the engineer's role is to monitor and supervise the construction and to ensure that the works are completed to time, cost and quality. The extent of the engineer's financial control may vary considerably with the type of contract. If a contract is for a fixed price, the engineer's capacity for controlling costs may be limited to minimizing the number and size of variations. If a contract is cost reimbursable the engineer usually has the power to direct the work and thus to influence its cost directly.

Setting rates and agreeing prices for new work

When additional work is required for which payment has not been provided in the contract documents, the engineer may have power either to agree new rates for measured work or a fixed price for a defined piece of work. Even if a quantity surveyor is involved, it will be the responsibility of the engineer to ensure that the rates or prices set represent good value for money to the client. The engineer makes decisions according to his or her powers and duties as laid down in the terms of the contract. In general it is expected that the engineer shall be fair and reasonable in the way he or she administers the contract.

Dayworks is a means of paying a contractor on a time and materials basis for incidental work to the contract to comply with the engineer's instructions, with additions for overheads and profit. Dayworks should be minimized as they provide no incentive for a contractor to be efficient because he or she is not responsible for the efficient use of resources, the profit is guaranteed and there may be a risk of double payment.

Keep good records

Claims may have significant effects on the cost of a project to the client. It is essential to keep good records to pursue or respond effectively to a claim, a matter which is covered in detail in chapter 7.

Cost reports

The client will usually require the engineer to inform him or her of the likely final cost of construction at regular intervals. The form of cost report (an example of which is given in Table 6.1) will vary between projects. This report should be in part a cost recording device, as well as a cost forecasting device and thus a powerful management aid. In the example given, 'original variance' records the difference between original budget cost and the estimated final cost given in the last report; 'current variance' records the difference between the latest approved budget and current estimated final cost. 'Estimated final cost' records paid and estimated costs to complete.

Specification

Occasionally contractors are unable or unwilling to supply a specified material or equipment. It is usually the responsibility of the engineer to approve the alternative offered by the contractor or to suggest a possible solution. There are often cost and quality effects in so doing. Substitution of specified material may increase or decrease costs to the employer and the engineer should ensure that the employer obtains a refund if a cheaper alternative is used. Whether or not the employer should pay the excess for a more expensive substitution depends on the circumstances of the case.

Contractor's ability to control costs during construction

The success and profitability of a contract will depend on the ability of a contractor to manage and control time, cost and quality effectively. Responsibility for cost control should rest with the site agent or contract manager.

Time planning

An essential starting point in cost control is the preparation of a realistic plan which sets out logically how the works are to be built and includes some contingency for unexpected events. A

85

Table 6.1. *Example of a cost report: £ thousand*

Description	Budget		Estimated final cost		Period change	Variance		Orders placed	Paid	Estimated cost to complete	Estimated final cost
	Original	Latest approved	Last report	Current		Original	Current				
Land acquisition and fees	8500	8500	8500	8500	0	0	0	8500	500	8000	8500
Enabling work	350	300	350	300	50	0	0	200	50	250	300
Foundations	1000	900	900	900	0	100	0	900	0	900	900
Building shell	17 500	17 500	17 500	17 500	0	0	0	17 500	0	17 500	17 500
Building fitout	4000	4000	4000	4000	0	0	0	0	0	4000	4000
External works/drainage	250	290	250	290	40	40	0	0	0	290	290
Telecommunications	200	200	200	200	0	0	0	50	0	200	200
Fixtures and fittings	100	100	100	100	0	0	0	0	0	100	100
Contingency	1600	1560	1600	1560	40	0	0	0	0	1560	1560
Fees	3800	3800	3800	3800	0	0	0	500	200	3600	3800
Total cost	37 300	37 150	37 120	37 150	50	150	0	27 650	750	36 400	37 150

realistic plan sets achievable targets against which progress can be monitored.

The level of detail and complexity of the plan should match both the complexity of the works, the level of control required and the contractor's ability to understand and maintain the plan. The creation of a model of the project which reflects time, cost and resources is a powerful tool for controlling costs, but there is little point in preparing a highly complex critical path network if only the author of the network understands how it works.

Planning for labour, plant and materials

The allocation of labour to particular activities in the contract programme is a skilled task which requires both a knowledge of what is to be done as well as the likely outputs of the people employed. The allocation of labour to activities can be plotted as a histogram which will invariably show peaks and troughs. This can be smoothed, either manually or by computer, to control costs, particularly if the resource is scarce or expensive.

Even on small contracts, plant costs may account for a significant proportion of total costs. On large projects, particularly in heavy civil engineering, effective plant selection is crucial for effective cost control and needs to be used and controlled to meet the overall project objectives.

If materials are not to hand when they are needed, progress suffers and costs to the contractor increase. If materials are procured too early, the supplier may have to be paid before a contractor is paid by the client which can lead to cash flow costs. Materials procurement and usage must be planned to the same level of detail as labour and plant.

Planning for other items

Most construction projects require some subcontractor involvement either because of the specialized nature of part of the work which the main contractor is unable to carry out or because the subcontractor can do the job at lower cost than the main contractor. The main contractor has to plan for subcontracted work just as seriously as for his or her own work. The main contractor will also have to make proper arrangements for control of operations on site, to monitor the quality of subcontracted work and to ensure compliance with regulatory requirements. In addition a contractor

87

should plan for the cost of overheads, which may represent a sizeable item of expenditure each month.

Payment

The method and timing of application for payment should be prescribed in the terms of a contract. It is sensible for a contractor to apply for payment for work done to a specified date to limit the amount of funding required. Under both the Institution of Civil Engineers' Conditions of Contract (fifth edition) and Joint Contracts Tribunal conditions the contractor may apply for payment for permanent work done to date and, depending on the terms of the contract, for purchase of goods off site (subject to title to the goods having passed to the employer). The value of the work done in some cases (although less frequently in industrial construction) is calculated from bills of quantities. A percentage, known as retention (which will be specified in the terms of the contract) is deducted to provide the employer with some protection against defects in the works. Under the Institution of Civil Engineers' Conditions of Contract (fifth edition), retention money is repaid to a contractor in two stages, the first within 14 days after the certificate of completion has been issued, the remainder within 14 days after the end of the period of maintenance.

Planning, monitoring and control

The objective of controlling project costs must not be viewed in isolation from the other objectives of controlling time and quality. Each aspect of a project must have a plan or standard to be monitored, against which are the budget for cost, programme for time and brief for performance. Information gathered from monitoring will result in decisions which need to be taken to maintain control of the project. The options for each decision need to be evaluated and when a decision is made the project plan for each aspect of the project should be updated.

7 Control of claims and dealing with financial disputes

A claim is a demand for something that is due. It can be for time or money or, more often, for both. Claims may be made both by contractors and consultants and the principles described here generally apply.

The incidence of claims has increased in recent years. This is largely because of faster construction and very competitive pricing which have made contractors more vulnerable to the financial effects of disruption. As a result they are less willing to accept the increasing costs caused by disruption and seek to recover them through claims.

Claims are frequently of great importance both to the contractor and the client. The manner and timing of settlement are equally significant. This is not only because of the need for a contractor to make money but also to achieve an acceptable cash flow and, ideally, to obtain more work from the same client in the future.

Preventing claims

The aim of an engineer should be to manage a project in such a way as to minimize the incidence and effect of claims and, more importantly, to prevent disputed claims. The maxim 'prevention is better than cure' is particularly apposite in this context. Disputed claims can be an unnecessary drag on effective management of construction projects in that they

- absorb an enormous quantity of the time and energy of trained staff in unproductive activity
- destroy the spirit of co-operation which should exist between members of the project team.

Unfortunately, with the increasing incidence of claims by

Table 7.1. Management actions to prevent disputed claims

Project stage	Management action to prevent disputes
Design	Ensure that the consultant/contractor boundary for design decisions is set at an appropriate level for the project.
Tender	Ensure that a complete and clear (although not necessarily immutable) statement of what the contractor is to be required to do is provided so that the work to be covered by the tender price is fully and clearly described. Make sure the tender is compatible with the duties of the consultant. Ensure that the documents issued at the time of tender are consistent with the form of contract. Use a form of contract which promotes team work and encourages forward-looking management and decision-making.
Construction	Ensure that site or progress meetings concentrate on making plans for the conduct of the remaining work and altering those plans to allow for new knowledge instead of concentrating on allocating blame for departures from previous plans. Ensure that communications around the team are effective especially with regard to plans for future work. Ensure that arrangements are made for working to plans and programmes and for modifying them in the light of unexpected new information. Ensure that the consequences of any variation are fully appreciated and quantified before the variation is instructed. Ensure the keeping and agreeing of comprehensive records.

contractors, whether justified or not, it is incumbent on an engineer to analyse unjustified claims with as much vigour as contractors use to pursue them.

Most disputes derive from management shortcomings, whether directly or through failure by managers to implement the contract in a thorough, objective and rational manner. Good managers

Table 7.2.   Records to be maintained on any project

The contract programme and subsequent revisions.

Agreed progress reports including start and finish dates for all completed activities and percentage complete for current activities.

Areas and materials available for work but not in hand.

Lack of progress in available areas.

The actual effect of significant variations on construction methods and programme.

Delivery of materials.

Plant, labour and supervision on site compared with anticipated resources.

Weather.

Progress photographs.

Details of all payments compared with anticipated payments.

Details of all variations, site instructions and dayworks, including date instructed, area affected, estimated value.

Date and content of requests for information.

Date and content of provision of information.

Details of all disputed items.

Details of contractor's errors, such as unsatisfactory work, poor supervision and management, failure to comply with contract requirements.

Any other contributions by the contractor or the client to delay or disruption.

Schedules of significant correspondence.

---

therefore take steps to ensure that their projects avoid claims which will be disputed. Some of the ways in which this may be achieved are shown in Table 7.1. Two items — the type of contract and the records kept — are of particular importance.

Type of contract

The procedures which are set in place when the contract is signed will create the atmosphere for the remainder of the project. Some contracts are specifically drafted to reduce the incidence of claims by promoting team work and by encouraging forward-looking management and decision-making. Roles and responsibilities are clarified and the contract documents themselves simplified. A procedure which adopts this approach and contains a form of agreement is the British Property Federation System for Building Design and Construction. A similar approach is followed in the specification for the Institution of Civil Engineers' proposed new style contract. Even if new style forms of contract cannot be used, it is often possible to write specific requirements into existing standard forms to promote co-operation.

Other requirements might be to agree the implications of a variation, in terms of time and cost, before it is instructed and to provide for keeping and agreeing contemporaneous records.

Records

To establish whether or not a claim submitted by a contractor is valid, and to dispute it successfully if it is not, the client must ensure that accurate records are kept on his or her behalf. This involves setting up a management information system to contain comprehensive records including those listed in Table 7.2.

Types of claim

Claims fall into the following categories

- claims based on the contract documents
- extra contractual (*ex gratia*) claims which arise out of hardship and which do not rely on the terms of a contract
- claims based on a breach of a common law duty of care
- *quantum meruit* (as much as is deserved) claims which seek payment for work done where the contract does not have a fixed price.

How claims arise

Generally claims arise when conditions change from those originally envisaged. With the exception of genuinely unforeseen circumstances, changes in conditions may be attributed to

- imprecise or inadequate contract documents
- lack of communication between the parties
- poor estimating
- differences of opinion.

Imprecise contract documents

The dangers of issuing specifications, a bill of quantities (if appropriate) and drawings in a rush without checking them thoroughly for consistency and accuracy are that

- the intention underlying the contract and work described will be understood differently by the client, the engineer and the contractor
- the level of unforeseen circumstances will be high
- the client may not obtain the project he or she thought had been commissioned
- claims will arise for extensions of time and money.

To avoid such claims it is essential that all parties to a contract are fully aware of its scope and intent. The contract documents must therefore be comprehensive, consistent and explicit. It is essential to spend sufficient time on preparation before going out to tender and to ensure that the allocation of risks between the parties is clearly stated in the contract documents.

A large proportion of small claims arise from errors and ambiguities in and omissions from contract documents. Typically, contractors claim that they did not and need not have allowed in their tender for doing the disputed work. The engineer may contend that the need for the work was clear in the original documents. Therefore clarity is essential in contract documents.

Lack of communication between the parties

The written documents of a contract will inevitably require oral explanation. Good communication is needed between

- the consultants and the client
- the engineer and the consultants

93

- the engineer and the contractor
- the contractor and subcontractors.

It is prudent to confirm oral communications in writing to ensure that a record of events is available. This is particularly important when discussions take place between different levels, for example between the engineer and the contractor's head office and between the resident engineer and the site agent.

Poor estimating

Even if the contract documentation is precise occasionally an estimator will make a mistake. Estimators often work against considerable time pressures and look for ways to win jobs and at the same time make a profit.

If an estimator makes a mistake or error of judgement a contractor may look for ways to recoup any shortfall. One option is to make a claim. It is therefore important to consider the possibility of poor estimating when examining a claim.

Differences of opinion

Differences of opinion are often the most difficult problem to resolve. The problem is particularly acute when the difference of opinion concerns the risk and contractual responsibilities of the client on the one hand and the contractor on the other. Entrenched positions may be established easily between the two with the result that claims are prepared and argued merely to prevent loss of face when in reality the matter could and should have been settled by discussion on site when the problems arose.

Claims procedure

The procedure for making a claim depends on the form of contract in use. In general the timing of any notice of an intention to submit a claim will be specified as will the person to whom the notice should be addressed. Table 7.3 shows the responsible person specified in a number of contracts in common use.

A notice of intention to submit a claim should comply with the requirements of the contract and, if possible

- state the clause(s) under which the application is made
- state that there is an entitlement to an extension of time and reimbursement of monies (as appropriate)

Table 7.3. Responsible person in different contracts

Form of Contract	Responsible Person
ICE Conditions of Contract 5th Edition (Institution of Civil Engineers)	Engineer
Fédération Internationale Des Ingénieurs — Conseils (FIDIC) Conditions of Contract 4th Edition	Engineer
Standard Form of Building Contract 1980 Edition (Private) (Joint Contracts Tribunal)	Architect
Standard Form of Building Contract 1980 Edition (Local Authorities with Quantities) (Joint Contracts Tribunal)	Supervising officer or architect
GC/Works/1-Edition 2 (Government Contracts)	Superintending officer
ACA Form of Building Agreement 1982 (Association of Consultant Architects)	Architect
British Property Federation System for Building Design and Construction	Client's representative

- describe the anticipated effect on progress and interference with the works
- state the measures proposed to remedy the delay, etc.

At this point, under the ICE Conditions of Contract (5th edition), the engineer should carry out one of the following actions

- require the contractor to estimate the cost of the proposed remedial measures
- approve the proposed measures (with modifications, if required)
- issue a written instruction on the action required
- order a suspension of the work under Clause 44
- issue a variation under Clause 51.

If the engineer agrees the claim, he or she will

- determine any extension of time under Clause 44

- under Clause 52(4), determine any payment, in accordance with Clause 60
- determine whether a profit element is payable.

If the contractor or the employer disputes the engineer's decision, the engineer is entitled, under Clause 66, to take the matter to arbitration.

Preparation of a claim

The preparation of a claim should not be the chore that it so often becomes. Accurate and comprehensive claims are prepared from data retained and used as management information and estimating source information. The key stages of preparation are to

- become familiar with all the facts as recorded in key documents, for example correspondence, meeting records, site measurements, wage sheets and plant invoices
- try to agree the facts with the engineer and/or contractor
- check the claim is in order with respect to time and/or documentation and that it complies with the contract
- use the records to prepare a case establishing
- responsibility for disturbance and delay or for extra work
- extension of time due
- payment due for disturbance and delay or extra work.

In most types of dispute the claim might take the following form

- title sheet with claim number and date, contractor's name, employer's name and contract name all recorded
- contents
- contract details: form and date of agreement, parties to the contract, tender value, date of possession and completion, liquidated damages and defects liability period
- for each disruptive event or each element of extra work, the clause(s) under which the claim is made and the facts to which it relates, including full quotations from contract documents
- supporting drawings and photographs, etc.

A few general points should be borne in mind when preparing a claim.

- It should always be submitted in accordance with the procedures prescribed in the contract.

- Some engineers prefer claims under the ICE Conditions of Contract to be based on Clause 14 programme and tender assumptions, providing that the tender assumptions are judged to be reasonable. It is therefore prudent (and may be beneficial) to agree the claim format at an early stage.

- The engineer may request, especially at the tender stage, full details of the proposed resources and the contractor's pricing notes. This may have a significant bearing on the scope and flexibility of approach used by the contractor in presenting the claim.

- A contractor could use the actual performance when not working under claim conditions to establish what should have been foreseeable. This may be useful in analysing disruption claims.

- The analysis and valuation of a claim often requires a very thorough knowledge of labour, plant and materials use with time. This can be particularly important in quantifying claims for site overheads.

- The real state of progress on site and the necessary and actual levels of resources (these are often two different levels).

Responsibility for disturbance and delay

One difficult aspect of assessing claims turns on the problem of shared responsibility. Suppose, for example, that a contractor is behind schedule for his or her own reasons. A variation order or some other delay caused by the client occurs at a time which does not cause additional delay or cost but which would have done so if the contractor had not already been behind schedule. The fact of lateness is clear; two reasons for it are present, one the responsibility of the client, the other of the contractor. Does this duality of cause affect responsibility for the delay? Is the client entitled to be relieved of responsibility on the basis that the contractor would have been late anyway? Is the contractor entitled to be relieved of responsibility on the basis that if the variation was going to be made in any event at that time, to have been further advanced in the contract programme would only have made it more expensive for the client?

There does not appear to be a clear answer in law to these questions. However, as the contractor is free to time the work within the contract period it would be illogical for the contractor to be able to claim the cost and time effects of an influence which might have caused further delay but did not in fact do so; and in the situation described it is likely that the first cause rules.

It follows that if a contractor can demonstrate that the resources available and those intended for use on site would enable the works to be finished early, the contractor would have good grounds for claiming reimbursement of additional costs if he or she was thwarted by the client's delay.

This logic has the advantage that it protects the more efficient contractor and exposes the less efficient and is thus conducive to efficiency in the long run. It also follows that the fact that a variation order has been issued after the contractual completion date does not necessarily provide grounds for an extension of time.

Quantification of the extension of time

The ICE Conditions of Contract entitle the contractor to an extension of time if any of a number of specified events delays the works. These include delay in the issue of drawings, instructions by the engineer, unforeseen physical conditions, delay by other contractors and delay in giving possession of the site. (Other contracts in common use contain some similar provisions.)

The timely award of an extension of time may avoid problems which might arise at a later stage when a contractor submits a claim for taking extraordinary measures to recover lost time owing to the late issue of an instruction, for example. An extension of time relieves the contractor of liability for liquidated damages for delays up to the new completion date caused by the occurrence of risks which are outside the contractor's responsibility. It does not entitle the contractor to additional money. However, events which entitle the contractor to an extension of time may also entitle the contractor to recover extra costs. It is therefore important, where possible, that any extension should be itemized against the individual event causing the delay and the clause number under which it is granted.

Analysing the programmes

Analysis of the contractor's programmes should begin at the tender stage so that from the onset of a contract the attainability of the programme (and thus the completion date) have been assessed.

Key features to check and validate are

- are activities shown as starting unnecessarily early?
- are activities overlapped to a greater extent than is practical?
- are activities unreasonably extended or curtailed?
- can the proposed labour and plant resources support the durations and sequencing of the activities?
- does the materials procurement programme dovetail with the construction programme?
- can the client meet the programme in terms of the timely supply of information?

Float (i.e. the lapse of time between the end of a work element and the following dependent work element) or a programmed period of unproductive time within a work element has to be recognized in both the tender and subsequent programmes. The contractor's provision of float within the programme is there to cover items that are at the contractor's own risk and in general should not be used to abate any extension of time to which the contractor may be entitled.

To aid the overall analysis of the contractor's programmes it is often appropriate to request at tender

- detailed programmes for each structure or major work area
- programmes for shutter, falsework and scaffolding erection and movement
- resource schedules against work elements, and movement charts for labour and plant.

When examining the programme, the engineer should look for

- compatibility of time/location charts and detailed programmes
- inclusion of all activities
- any specified sequences of work
- out of season work
- proper allowance for all restraints
- compatibility between resources and outputs
- the type and level of resources anticipated.

Delays may then be analysed by comparing the foreseeable construction programme and resources with those actually used. Providing that the construction logic is understood, this can be done by

- preserving work sequences in activities
- observing seasonal working patterns
- preserving the contractor's float between operations
- analysing other resource criticalities (such as plant, shutter movements and gang movements).

Delay due to disruption

With delays caused by disturbance to the regular progress of the works it is often very difficult to tie cause and effect together with any certainty. Delay in the completion of one work element which prevents the start of the next where the same plant and labour are used can easily be demonstrated. An example is the use of a crane to move shutters on one structure and the subsequent use of the crane for moving skips of concrete to a second structure.

However, there are often delaying factors that can only be substantiated by a thorough analysis of the records referred to in Table 7.2. Such factors include

- *Reduced utilization.* This is when there is an increase in idle time, that is to say, when the smooth flow of resources from one construction activity to the next does not occur as planned. The associated additional cost arises from either
- o people and equipment standing idle while instructions are awaited, or
- o working at a reduced rate on other activities, therefore increasing durations of these activities.

- *Reduced productivity.* This is a reduction in the quantity of work done in the relevant period by the same resources. Reasons for a reduction in productivity may include
- o a poorly planned operation which can result in longer learning curves and a low average output
- o the introduction of more learning curves because of frequent changes of resources and working methods
- o changing physical conditions
- o lower outputs because plant was initially selected for one activity and is used for another inappropriate activity
- o longer hours being worked regularly (this can occur, for example, when accelerating the work rate to recover delays)
- o the lowering of morale owing to frequent changes of plan and poor management.

The increasing time pressure due to reduced utilization and productivity will itself increase demands on both site and off-site management.

The effect of these features of disruption is cumulative. The length of the delay will depend on

- the severity of the time and change effects
- the plant intensive nature of the work
- the inflexibility of the resource teams available
- the length of time between changes or delays arising, and the work being carried out.

Working out the cost of disturbance

Claims are rarely as simple as the type of situation envisaged in Clause 12 of the ICE Conditions of Contract (5th edition) producing a readily identified effect that can be costed easily. Commonly claims range over a number of 'points of claim' resulting in a large number of 'heads of damage' under which the contractor claims to have suffered loss. It is not sufficient to assess the delay to critical activities and multiply this by the preliminaries or overhead costs. Such a calculation is unlikely to produce a sum of money anywhere near the true cost of disturbance. Fortunately arbitrators and the courts have recognized that it is often not possible in a complicated situation to relate a particular cause to effect: see the remarks of Mr Justice Donaldson in *J Crosby & Sons* v. *Portland UDC* [1976] 5 BLR 121.

A justifiable claim depends on loss being sustained in circumstances envisaged by the contract. The contractor's financial remedy will be defined in the contract. This should also include the cost of funding any additional money required to complete the work.

There are two rules as to the admissibility or otherwise of a contractor's claim

- the contractor must produce evidence that additional costs were actually incurred
- the contractor must prove that the additional costs incurred were reasonable in the circumstances.

When the engineer checks the claim, he or she needs to ensure that additional costs are not claimed twice, for example additional

101

costs already recovered by additional measured work or dayworks or variations priced at current prices.

One method of calculating the value of a claim is to consider separately the cost of materials, plant, labour, temporary works and indirect costs. Each major site operation or resource type should be considered separately in terms of utilization, productivity and any premium costs of overtime or additional resources. However, it is important to consider the interaction of events because instances of disturbance will have greater or lesser effects on cost depending on the actual timing and the method of working of the contractor.

A disturbance claim which includes only cost increasing effects is suspect. For example among all the delays which push work into the winter period there must be some which push it out of the other end of winter into summer. Among the extra work which required a special piece of plant to be brought onto the site for one week and then returned 200 miles, there must be some extra work which just happens to be within the scope of a piece of plant which is already on site which would otherwise have been idle during the week in question.

Providing that the grounds for the claim are clear and all necessary records are available, calculation of the additional cost for time related charges only should be relatively straightforward.

Overheads

Head office overheads attributable to a particular site are difficult to calculate because many head office staff are involved in a multitude of contracts. For example, it would be very difficult to divide a telephonist's time between particular contracts. Nevertheless it is possible to apportion head office overheads to a particular contract by comparing total company turnover and contract turnover and their proportion to total head office overheads in the same ratio, thus

$$\text{contract proportion of head office overheads} = \frac{\text{contract turnover}}{\text{company turnover}} \times \text{head office overheads}$$

Further methods of calculating head office overheads attributable to a particular contract are described in the publications listed in the bibliography.

Site overheads may be included in the tender sum in various

ways, for example in the preliminaries, in a balancing item and as a percentage of rates across some or all of the items.

In awarding an extension of time and then, if appropriate, calculating any overheads due to be reimbursed, allowance should be made for any overheads already recouped through additional work items instructed which contributed to the extension of time.

A method of calculating additional overhead expenditure is as follows. Calculate the cost of each overhead against the foreseeable programme of works (for example, cost of the project manager for six months, one tower crane for two months, accommodation for eight months) to produce a graph of overhead costs against time which is checked against the tender programme. Then repeat the calculations for the actual construction programme, making due allowance for exceptionally adverse weather and delays which are at the contractor's risk. Payment is due for these delays under the terms of the contract. Then subtract the former costs from the latter costs to obtain the reimbursable overheads cost. Any method of calculating the cost of additional overheads is contentious, as there is no universally accepted method, other than keeping records of actual costs.

Labour and plant

Labour and plant disruption is likely to have the greatest impact on the contractor's cost but it is invariably the most difficult to substantiate and evaluate. The contractor's ability to demonstrate cause and effect will depend to a large extent on the effectiveness of the financial and management procedures. The contractor's system should allow cost/value comparisons to be made for parts of the project rather than for the project as a whole.

An effective way of calculating the additional costs relating to plant and labour, which can usually be treated together, is to identify an undisrupted part of the project. The earnings against expenditure achieved in this area can then be used as a control against which the costs of disrupted areas can be compared and entitlement to additional costs identified.

Financing costs

The calculation of additional financing costs may also be carried out on a comparative basis, comparing what the costs would have been had the project not been delayed and disrupted compared with actual costs. Schedules for each case should be prepared showing the month by month differences between actual costs and the cost included in interim payments, from which the extra costs of funding can be calculated.

Computer modelling

On a large contract one of the most cost effective methods of calculating the total cost of disruption is to use a computer. In general terms the methodology is as follows.

- *Step 1:* Prepare a comprehensive model of the actual recorded contract progress with actual costs, time and resources allocated against activities.

- *Step 2:* Deduct extra costs, time and resources incurred owing to claimable events from the contract model.

- *Step 3:* Test the model resulting from step 2 for artificial constraints and any mis-statements of logic and produce a new cost and time model representing what should have happened during the performance of the contract.

This method allows the difference to be calculated between the actual costs described in the first step and the costs described in the third step, i.e. those which should have been incurred and foreseen. The difference represents the actual cost of disruption.

The amount of detail described by the computer model may vary but the contract activities must be split into sufficiently small parts to allow realistic analysis and modelling of all the significant relationships between different parts of the works. For example, if the number of tower cranes on site is critical, all tower crane movements must be separately identified in the computer model.

Settlement

The key factors involved in achieving a satisfactory settlement are

- agreement of the facts of the claim with the engineer
- the timing of the settlement: this may well be influenced by the contractor's actual and predicted cash flow
- the authority of the negotiating team: make sure the other side in any negotiation has complete authority to negotiate and to settle

- only agree settlement of a single claim item subject to a satisfactory overall settlement: a skilled negotiator can pick off the strong points in a claim and attempt to buy them cheaply
- knowing the acceptable upper and lower limits for a settlement: before starting any negotiations set the maximum and minimum limits which are acceptable.

Bibliography

Abrahamson M.W. *Engineering law and the ICE contracts*. Applied Science Publishers, London, 1979, 4th edn.

Allen M.W. and Myddelton D.R. *Essential management accounting*. Prentice Hall, London, 1987.

Armstrong W.E.I. *Contractual claims under the ICE conditions of contract*. Chartered Institute of Building, London.

British Property Federation. *Manual of the British Property Federation — the British Property Federation system for building design and construction*. BPF, 1983.

Companies Act 1985. HMSO, London.

Davies M.C. *Avoiding claims — a practical guide for the construction industry*. E&F Spon, 1989.

Foster G. *Financial statement analysis*. Prentice Hall, London, 1986, 2nd edn.

Harvey D.A. and Nettleton M. *Management accounting*. Mitchell Beazley, London, 1983.

Haswell C.K. and de Silva *Civil engineering contracts — practice and procedure*. Butterworths, London, 1982.

Hayes R.W. *et al. Risk management in engineering construction*. Thomas Telford, London, 1987.

Horngren C.T. and Foster G. *Cost accounting — a management emphasis*. Prentice Hall, London, 1987, 6th edn.

Horngren C.T. and Sundem G.L. *Introduction to financial accounting*. Prentice Hall, London, 1987, 3rd edn.

Horngren C.T. and Sundem G.L. *Introduction to management accounting*. Prentice Hall, London, 1987, 7th edn.

Institute of Chartered Accountants in England and Wales. *Statement of Standing Accounting Practice*. ICA, SSAP 1–6, 8–10, 12–18, 20.

Institute of Chartered Accountants in England and Wales. *Statements of Recommended Practice*. ICA.

International Accounting Standards Committee. *International Accounting Standards*. IASC, IAS 1–13.

Johnson B and Patient M. *Accounting provisions of the Companies Act 1985*. Farringdon Publishing, London, 1985.

Merrett A.J. and Sykes A. *The finance and analysis of capital projects*. Longman, London, 1973, 2nd edn.

Merrett A.J. and Sykes A. *Capital budgeting and company finance*. Longman, London, 1973, 2nd edn.

Powell Smith V. and Stephenson D. *Civil engineering claims*. BSP Professional Books, London, 1989.

Reid W. and Myddelton D.R. *The meaning of company accounts*. Gower, London, 1982, 3rd edn.

Tolley. *Annual tax guides: capital gains tax; corporation tax; income tax; value added tax*. Tolley Publishing Company, London.

Wallace I.N.D. *Construction contracts: principles and policies in tort and contract*. Sweet and Maxwell, London, 1986.

Wallace I.N.D. *The ICE conditions of contract 5th edition: a commentary*. Sweet and Maxwell, London, 1978.

Wearne S.H. *Civil engineering contracts*. Thomas Telford, London, 1989.

Wearne S.H. (ed.) *Control of engineering projects*. Thomas Telford, London, 1989, 2nd edn.

Wood R.D. *Building and civil engineering claims*. Estates Gazette, 1985, 3rd edn.

Wood R.D. *Contractor's claims under GC/Works/1 Edition 2*. Chartered Institute of Building, London, 1986.

Biographies

Martin Barnes, *BSc, PhD, FEng, FICE, FCIOB, CBIM*
Martin Barnes is a partner in the management consultancy of Coopers & Lybrand Deloitte and has responsibility for the engineering and construction project management assignments of the Construction and Property Group.

He has been active in the field of financial control of civil engineering projects for many years and is well known as the author of the *Civil engineering standard method of measurement*. He has advised on the management of many substantial projects including the Scheldt Barrier in the Netherlands and the Cairo wastewater scheme.

He is a frequent lecturer on engineering project management and designed the distinctive training course in this subject which he runs annually for the Institution of Civil Engineers at the Outward Bound Centre at Eskdale in the Lake District. Dr Barnes is also chairman of the Association of Project Managers.

Eur Ing **C.A. Cree,** *BSc, PhD, MICE, ACIArb*
Caroline Cree is a principal associate in the Construction and Property Group of the Coopers & Lybrand Deloitte management consultancy. After Dr Cree graduated in civil engineering, she undertook research in fluid dynamics at the University of Leeds. Dr Cree completed her professional training with Watson Hawksley, consulting engineers, where she concentrated on public health engineering and specialist hydraulics design. Subsequently she joined R.M. Douglas Construction Limited where she dealt with contractual disputes, contract administration and planning.

Since moving into consultancy, Dr Cree has continued to work on contractual claims and associated aspects of construction,

108

including cost control, contract strategy and contract audit and troubleshooting. Dr Cree has also acquired extensive experience of project feasibility studies for both funding agencies and project sponsors.

M. Hatcher, *MA, Barrister*

Mark Hatcher is a senior associate in the Construction and Property Group of the Coopers & Lybrand Deloitte management consultancy. After taking his degree in law at Oxford, Mr Hatcher was called to the Bar by the Middle Temple in 1978. In 1980 he joined the Law Commission before moving in 1983 to the Lord Chancellor's Department to work on the formulation of legal policy. He was assistant secretary of the Lord Chancellor's Law Reform Committee from 1984 to 1988.

Mr Hatcher has acquired a wide-ranging experience of English and international legal problems in different contexts including construction, engineering and the environment.

M. Jackson, *MA, ACA*

Molly Jackson is a principal associate with the Management Strategy Group of the Coopers & Lybrand Deloitte management consultancy. She qualified as an accountant and has acquired extensive experience in feasibility studies, project development and project financing.

Miss Jackson has used her project appraisal and financing skills on a number of international construction projects including assignments in Austria, the Middle East and the USA, working for a variety of clients in the public and private sectors. She is currently working with a client to develop a chain of country house hotels along the eastern seaboard of the USA, acting as overall business adviser as well as assisting with the arrangement of finance.

E. McEwan, *BSc, CA*

Euan McEwan is a principal associate in the Construction and Property Group of the Coopers & Lybrand Deloitte management consultancy. He started an apprenticeship with W.A. Fairhurst and Partners, consulting engineers, in Glasgow before taking a sandwich degree in civil engineering at Paisley College of Technology. He then completed a postgraduate course in accountancy at Strathclyde University and trained as a chartered accountant with Alexander Sloan and Co. (Glasgow). On qualifying as a chartered accountant, he moved to Deloitte Haskins & Sells, Glasgow, before joining their consultancy division in London.

With Coopers & Lybrand Deloitte Construction and Property Group, Mr McEwan specializes in advising clients on the various business implications of their construction and property activities.

J.M. Morris, *BSc, MBA, MICE, MIStructE*

Jeff Morris is a principal associate in the Construction and Property Group of the Coopers & Lybrand Deloitte management consultancy. He graduated from Nottingham University in 1974 and joined Kenchington, Little and Partners as a structural engineer. He became a chartered civil engineer and chartered structural engineer in 1978. He has worked for contractors, including French Keir, as a site agent. Mr Morris has been responsible for the site management of a variety of projects. In 1983 he joined Martin Barnes & Partners (now part of Coopers & Lybrand Deloitte) as client's project manager. He has managed a number of projects in different sectors (including retail, research laboratories, a computer centre and hotel and leisure) ranging from feasibility studies to client commissioning.

Mr Morris is currently responsible for managing consultancy assignments, including project management, contractual claims and urban regeneration.

M. Richardson, *MA, MBA, MICE*

Mark Richardson is a principal in the Construction and Property Group of the Coopers & Lybrand Deloitte management consultancy. After graduating in engineering from the University of Cambridge, he worked with Sir M. MacDonald and Partners, consulting engineers, as project engineer/design engineer preparing feasibility studies, detailed designs and contract documents for civil engineering projects in Cyprus, Indonesia, Oman, Somalia and the UK.

Since Mr Richardson moved into management consultancy in 1984, he has specialized in the planning, cost control and management of large projects and capital programmes. His experience also extends to project appraisal, contract troubleshooting and urban regeneration projects.

Mr Richardsons's clients include British Airways, British

Waterways Board, Dubal Aluminium Co. and the development corporations of London Docklands, Merseyside and Sheffield.

S. Roberts, *BA, MSc*

Simon Roberts is the partner who leads the property side of the Construction and Property Group of the Coopers & Lybrand Deloitte management consultancy.

After graduating from Reading University in Economics, Mr Roberts worked in operational research at the National Coal Board and then obtained an MSc in operational research. After ten years with P&O SN Co., where Mr Roberts was involved in acquisitions, disposals, development projects and corporate planning, he joined Deloitte Haskins and Sells (now Coopers & Lybrand Deloitte).

Since then he has worked on a wide range of public and private sector projects in the property area. These have included property developments, property management, strategy, financial appraisal, finance and management information systems, and urban regeneration projects. His clients include British Waterways Board, Commission for New Towns, Department of the Environment, Marks and Spencer, Prudential Property Managers and Tarmac Properties.

Eur Ing **G.B. Wylie,** *BSc, ACGI, MSc, DIC, MBA, MICE, MIStructE*

Gordon Wylie is an associate in the Construction and Property Group of the Coopers & Lybrand Deloitte management consultancy. After completing a BSc in civil engineering and MSc in concrete structures at Imperial College, Mr Wylie joined the Building Engineering Division of Ove Arup & Partners in 1982. His design office experience covered a wide variety of buildings involving reinforced concrete, structural steelwork, load-bearing masonry, timber and foundation design in multi-disciplinary projects. As a site resident engineer, which included working on the Lloyds redevelopment project, he gained experience of site works and procedures.

Mr Wylie graduated from the MBA programme at INSEAD, in Paris, in 1988. Since moving into management consultancy in 1989 he has been involved in a number of assignments including a preliminary feasibility study for a hotel and leisure complex, the preparation of a grant submission to the European Commission

111

on behalf of a UK local authority and a major option appraisal for a scientific research and postgraduate teaching centre.

Index